Collections for Young Scholars™

STEP–BY–STEP PRACTICE STORIES

GRADE 1

PROGRAM AUTHORS
Marilyn Jager Adams
Carl Bereiter
Jan Hirshberg
Valerie Anderson

CONSULTING AUTHORS
Michael Pressley
Marsha Roit
Iva Carruthers
Bill Pinkney

OPEN COURT PUBLISHING COMPANY

Cover art by Nelle Davis
Composition, electronic page makeup, and art management were provided by
Chestnut House Group, Inc.

Printed in the United States of America

ISBN 0-8126-1243-4

18 17

Contents

About the Step-by-Step Practice Stories

The Step-by-Step Practice Stories allow your students to apply their knowledge of phonic elements to read simple, engaging texts. Each story supports instruction in a new phonic element and incorporates elements and words that have been learned earlier. The Step-by-Step Practice Stories differ from the Phonics Minibooks in that they incorporate only one new element at a time, while the minibooks reinforce several recently learned elements.

The students can fold and staple the pages of each Step-by-Step Practice Story to make books of their own to keep and read. We suggest that you keep extra sets of the stories in your classroom for the children to reread.

In addition to the story pages, you will find letters that the students can take home to their families. These letters tell what sounds and spellings are reinforced in each story and suggest family activities that will support reading.

For a complete discussion of reading the Step-by-Step Practice Stories with your students, see Learning Framework Card 6.

How to Make a Step-by-Step Practice Story book

1. Tear out the pages you need.

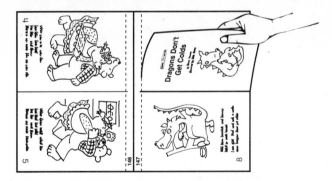

2. Place pages 4 and 5 and pages 2 and 7 face up.

3. Place pages 4 and 5 on top of pages 2 and 7.

4. Fold along the center line.

5. Check to make sure that the pages are in order.

6. Staple the pages at the staple marks.

Just to let you know . . .

This year your child will be learning to read with Open Court's *Collections for Young Scholars*™. From time to time your child will bring home his or her very own Step-by-Step Practice Story books to share with you. With your help, these stories can give your child important reading practice and a joyful shared reading experience.

You may want to set aside a few minutes every evening to read these Step-by-Step Practice Stories together. Here are some suggestions you may find helpful:

- Do not expect your child to read each story perfectly, but concentrate on sharing the book together.
- Participate by doing some of the reading.
- Talk about the stories as you read, give lots of encouragement, and watch as your child becomes more fluent throughout the year!

Step-by-Step Practice Stories 1–5 provide practice with the following reading concepts:

Story 1 — introduction to reading Step-by-Step Practice Stories

Story 2 — introduction to reading Step-by-Step Practice Stories

Story 3 — short *a* (as in *hat*)

Story 4 — short *a* (as in *man*)

Story 5 — short *a* (as in *cat*)

Tear off the following activity and either post it on your refrigerator or keep it where you can refer to it to practice reading and writing with your child.

REFRIGERATOR ACTIVITY

Finger Printing

You need: a shallow pan or tray

               sand, salt, or shaving cream

What to do: Pour a thin layer of sand, salt, or shaving cream in the tray. As you name a letter, have your child practice writing the letter with his or her finger. Practice both capital and small letters.

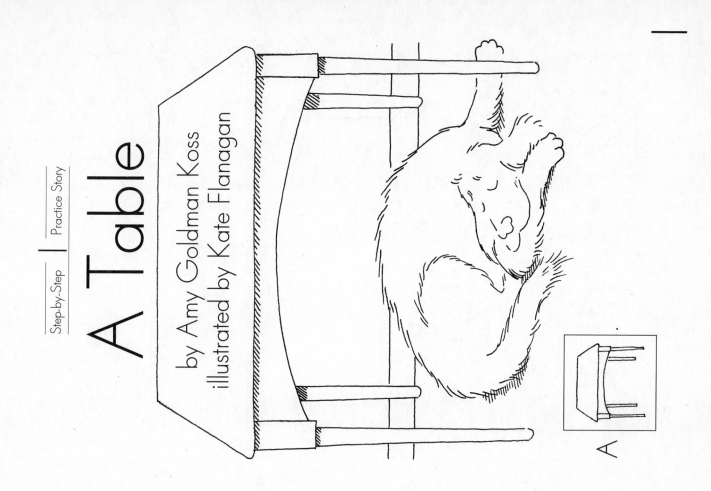

A Table

by Amy Goldman Koss
illustrated by Kate Flanagan

A

A

8

A 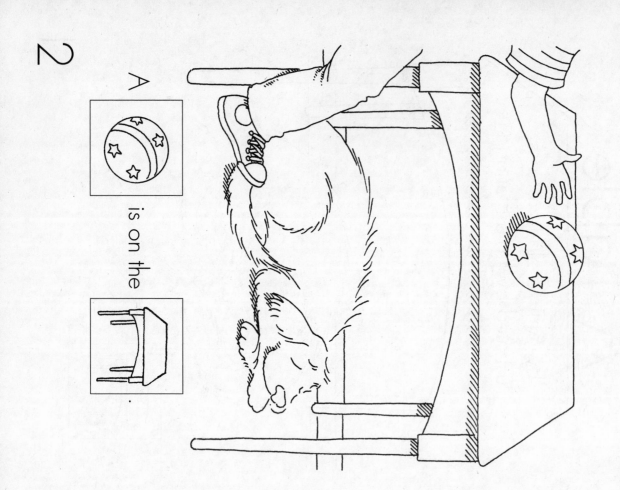 is on the [ ].

A  is on the

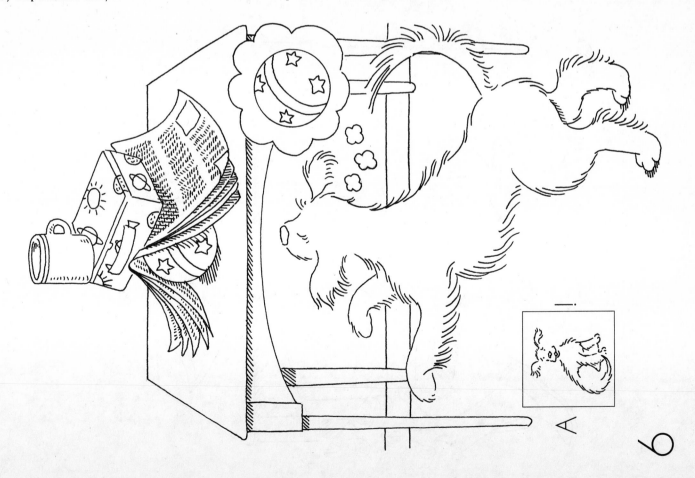

A !

4

A 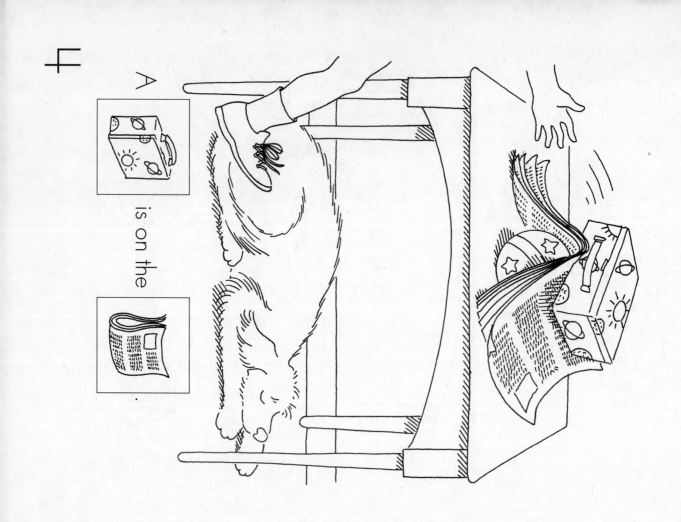 is on the ___ .

5

A ___ is on the ___ .

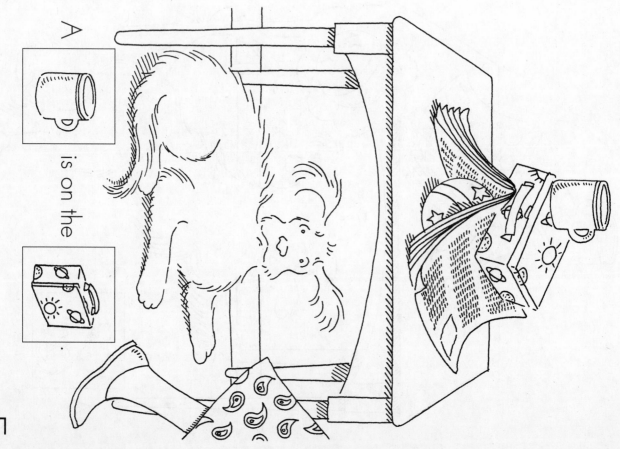

The farmer put Hank in a box.
She put the box in her van.
On the way to the market,
she stopped at a bank.

A robber ran out of the bank.
He jumped into the van!
Hank's box tipped over.
Hank flapped out of the box.
He was _very_ cranky!

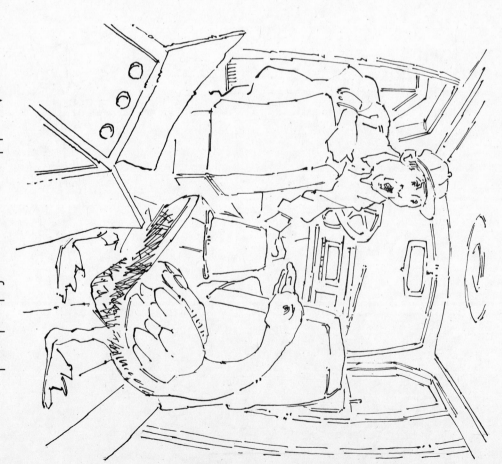

"Hank, I think it's time to sell you,"
said the farmer.
Hank honked and hissed.

3

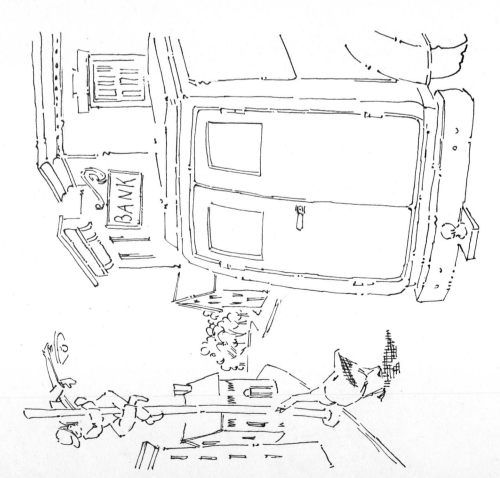

Hank kept honking and hissing.
He ran after the robber
and chased him up a lamp.

6

In the dark, Hank stopped honking.
But if something woke Hank,
he made such a racket
that no one on the farm could sleep.

The police got the robber.
The farmer got Hank.
The police thanked Hank,
but the robber thanked the farmer!

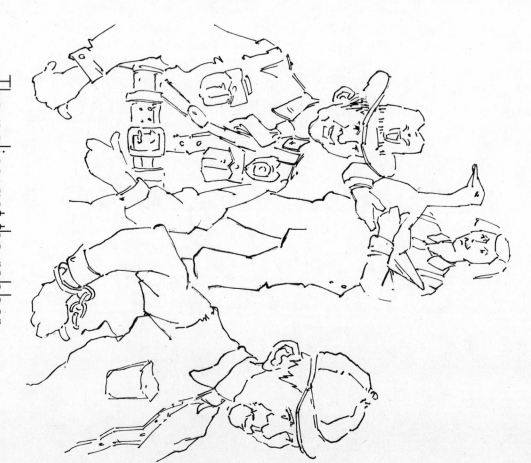

Cranky Hank

by Robert R. O'Brien

illustrated by John Fulweiler

Hank was cranky.

He was always honking and hissing.

He even honked at the farmer.

1

"Well, Hank," said the farmer.

"You are a hero.

Your honking saved the day.

Every farm needs a hero,

even a cranky one!"

8

"Bly, why do you stick your head
in the sand?" cries Chimp.
"Why not climb a tree like me?"

"I do not want to climb trees," Bly replies.
"I like myself the way I am."

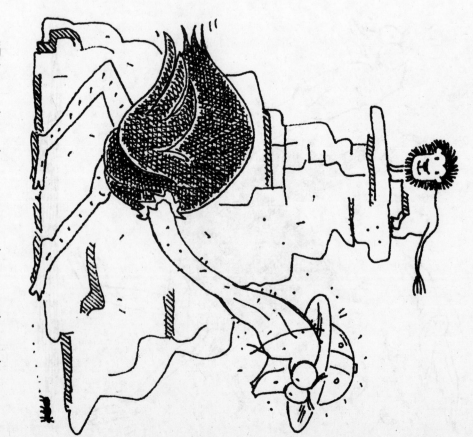

"Bly, why do you stick your head
in the sand?" cries Lion.
"Why not hunt like me?"

"I do not want to hunt," Bly replies.
"I like myself the way I am."

"Bly, why do you stick your head
in the sand?" cries Snake.
"Why not lie in the sun like me?"

"I do not want to lie in the sun," Bly replies.
"I like myself the way I am."

3

"Bly, why do you stick your head
in the sand?" cries Eagle.
"Why not fly in the sky like me?"

"I am too big to fly," replies Bly.
"I like myself the way I am."

6

Bly is an ostrich.
She has a small head.
She likes to stick her head in the sand.
The animals feel that Bly is an odd bird.

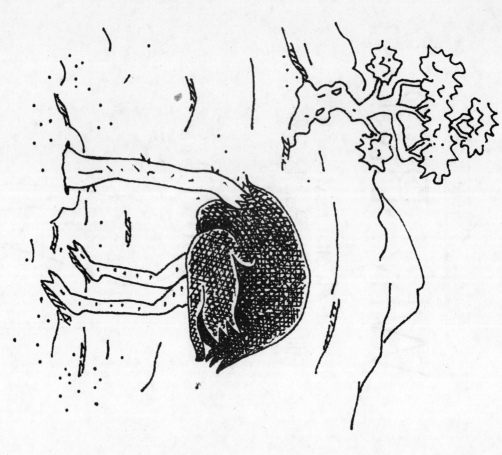

2

"Bly, why do you stick your head
in the sand? Are you shy?"
"Are you shy?" cries a child.

"I am not shy," Bly replies.

7

Step-by-Step 39 Practice Story

Why, Bly?

by Dottie Raymer
illustrated by Bob Barner

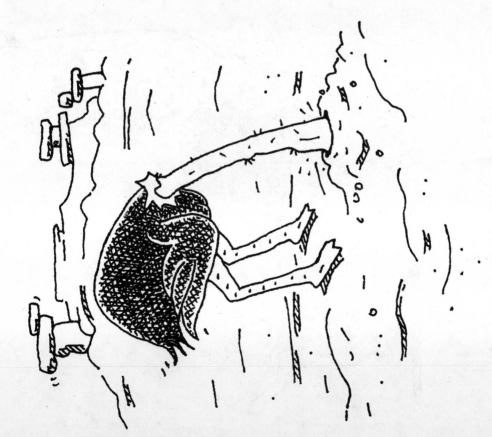

"It is hot and dry out here," Bly says.
"I feel better in the sand.
I will stay just the way I am."

8

The opossum does not wake up.
She sleeps in the daylight.
Her babies hold on tight.

2

When it is night, she wakes.
She hunts for insects to feed her babies.
Freeze! A dog frightens the opossum.
The opossum plays dead.
She "plays possum."

3

The Opossum

by Anne O'Brien

illustrated by Sharron O'Neil

It is light.
"Wake up! Wake up!" the birds call.
"The sun is high. The day is bright.
Wake up!"

1

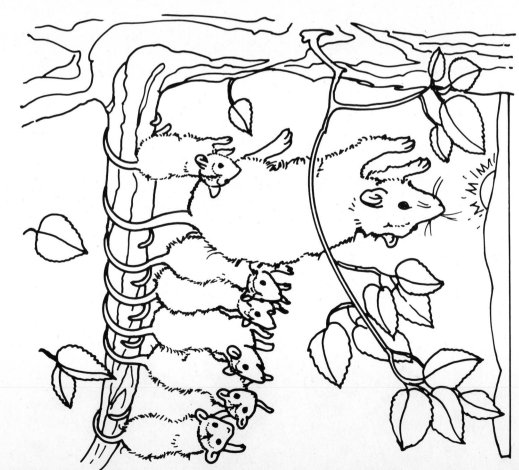

Night is over. It begins to get light.
The opossum returns to her tree.
"Go to sleep," she tells her babies.
"We will play again tonight."

4

"Oh, I'm not afraid of rain.
We can sail in rain!"

"We can sail, but we must be safe,"
said Mrs. Fay. "Stay here, Ray.
I'll check the main."

"The main?" said Ray.
"Do you mean the big sail?
I can help raise it!"

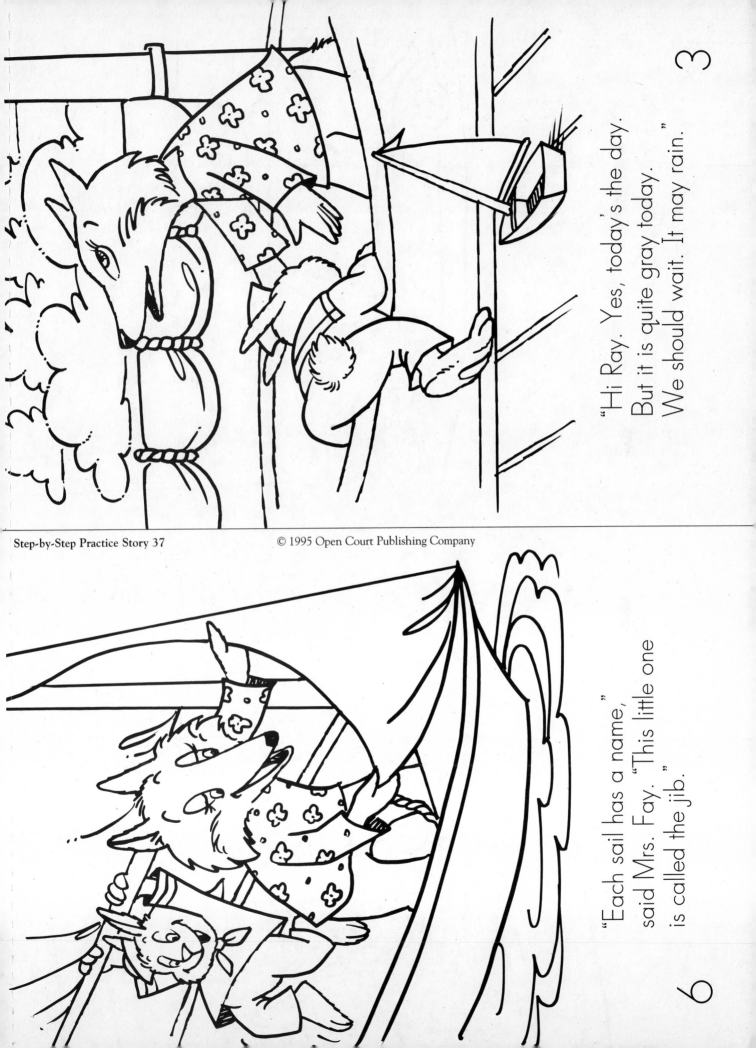

"Hi Ray. Yes, today's the day.
But it is quite gray today.
We should wait. It may rain."

© 1995 Open Court Publishing Company

"Each sail has a name,"
said Mrs. Fay. "This little one
is called the jib."

"Mrs. Fay! Mrs. Fay!
Today's the day!
Today I get to sail!"

2

"The main? The jib?
Well, I just want to sail."

7

Sail Day

by Alice Cary

illustrated by Anne Kennedy

SAILING SCHOOL

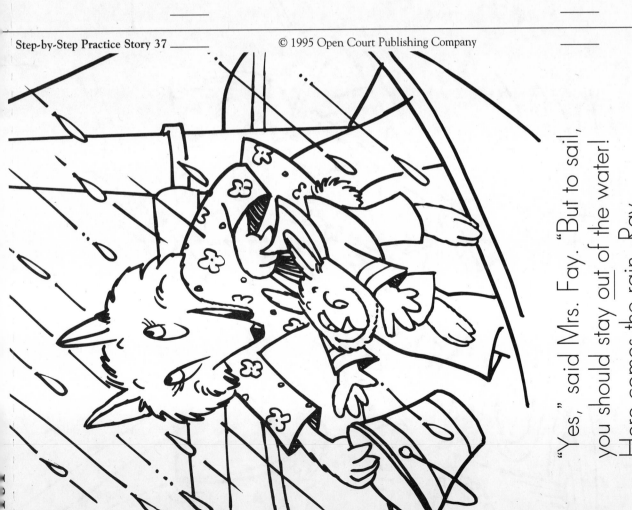

"Yes," said Mrs. Fay. "But to sail,
you should stay out of the water!
Here comes the rain, Ray.
Grab a pail! It's time to bail!"

8

Just to let you know . . .

By now, your child has probably collected a good-sized library of Step-by-Step Practice Stories. Remember to give your child plenty of opportunities to reread these little books to you, to a younger brother or sister, to other children or adults, or even to the family pet!

Step-by-Step Practice Stories 37–40 will focus on the following sounds and spellings:

Story 37 — long *a* spelled *ai, ay* (as in *sail* and *day*)

Story 38 — long *i* spelled *igh* (as in *high*)

Story 39 — long *i* spelled *y* (as in *why*)

Story 40 — *ing, nk* (as in *honking*)

Tear off the following activity and post it on your refrigerator where you can refer to it to practice reading with your child.

- -

REFRIGERATOR ACTIVITY

My Own Step-by-Step Practice Story

You need: a sheet of paper

What to do: Fold the sheet of paper in half to make a four-page book. With your child, choose a spelling, such as *qu* or *ee,* and brainstorm a list of words that contain that spelling. Have your child make up a story using as many of those words as possible. Help him or her write the story on the book pages, leaving room on each page for an illustration.

4

Nelly gets her baby dolls and teddies.
Willy carries them to the table.
Willy's puppies help.

5

Nelly makes funny party hats.
Willy tapes ribbons onto each hat.
Willy's puppies help.

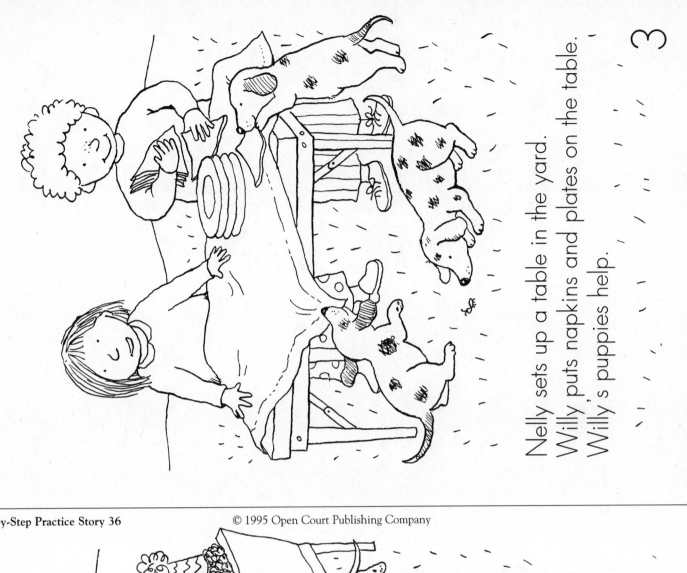

Nelly sets up a table in the yard.
Willy puts napkins and plates on the table.
Willy's puppies help.

3

Nelly has berries from the garden.
Willy puts a big berry on every plate.
Willy's puppies help.

6

Nelly and Willy like to have fancy parties.
They invite Nelly's baby dolls and teddies.
Today they have invited
Willy's puppies, too.

2

Nelly gets out the candy and ice cream.
Willy begins to put ice cream on the plates.
"No more help, please!"
Nelly tells the puppies.

7

The Fancy Party

by Anne O'Brien

illustrated by Julie Durrell

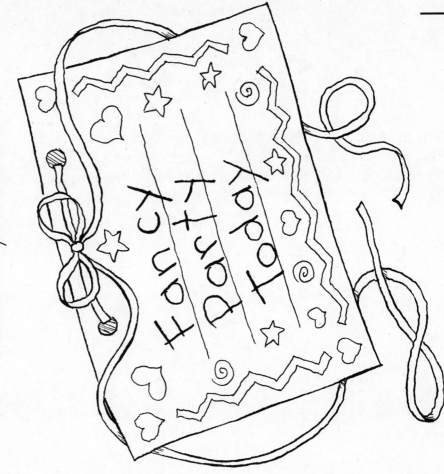

1

The fancy party is over.
The babies and teddies are muddy.
The candy is dirty. The party hats are torn.
Happy puppies lap up the ice cream.
"Thanks for the help," Willy tells his puppies.

8

The queen's squad of sea pals
heard her squeal.
"It's time for the queen's meal,"
said the pals.

The squad swam to get
the queen her meal.
A quiet shark swam near them.
He needed a meal, too.

The huge queen squid squealed,
"I need a meal!"

3

This time, the squad squealed!
The queen heard the squeals.

6

A huge queen squid lived
in the deep dark sea.
This kind queen squid
had a squad of sea pals to help her.

The quick queen swam to her pals.
She squirted black liquid
into the shark's face.
The shark swam away.

Queen Squid and Her Sea Pals

by Sandy Loose

illustrated by Liz Callen

1

The queen squid had saved her sea pals.
The shark had no meal.
The queen squid and her pals
had quite a feast!

8

"A cold!" creaked Deana.
"Dragons don't get colds!"

"You have a cold, Deana,"
said Deana's dad.
"You need to go to bed."

"I don't need to go to bed,"
creaked Deana.
"Dragons don't get colds.
Dragons breathe flames.
Dragons don't get colds!"

Deana's dad felt her cheeks.
"You feel hot," he said.
"You have a fever.
You must have a cold."

3

"Can you breathe flames?" asked Dad.

"Well, no," creaked Deana.

Dad made a pot of tea.
"The heat will help you breathe," he said.

6

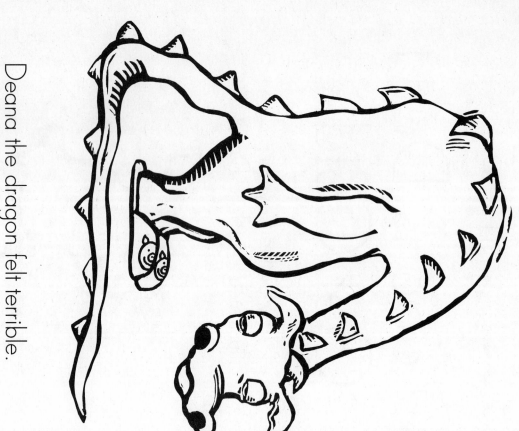

Deana the dragon felt terrible.
"I feel weak," said Deana.
"My nose hurts, and I can't breathe.
I can't speak. I just creak!"

"Dragons don't like tea," creaked Deana.

"Sip it," said Dad. "We will see."

The steam tickled Deana's nose.
"Dragons don't . . . AH! . . . get . . .
AH! . . . colds! . . . ACHOOO!"
Deana sneezed a big sneeze.

Dragons Don't Get Colds

by Dottie Raymer

illustrated by Nelle Davis

1

"Oh! I can breathe!" said Deana.
"I feel so much better!"

"I am glad," Dad said with a smile,
"since dragons don't get colds."

8

"What size is it?" asked Eve.
"Is it little? Is it big?"
"It is little," said Steve.
"But it is my secret. Do not even ask."

4

"What shape is it?" asked Eve.
"Is it flat? Is it tall?"
"It is flat," said Steve.
"But it is my secret. Let me be."

45

"What is in your pocket?" asked Eve.
"An acorn? A stone?"
"It is a secret," said Steve.
"It is for me."

© 1995 Open Court Publishing Company

"What shade is it?" asked Eve.
"Is it white? Is it red?"

Steve had a secret.
He hid it in his pocket.

"You will find out,"
said Steve with a smile.
"Then the secret will be yours and mine."

Steve's Secret

by Amy Goldman Koss

illustrated by Suçie Stevenson

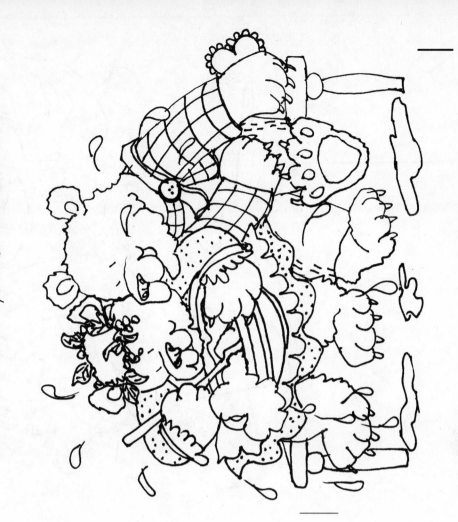

1

© 1995 Open Court Publishing Company

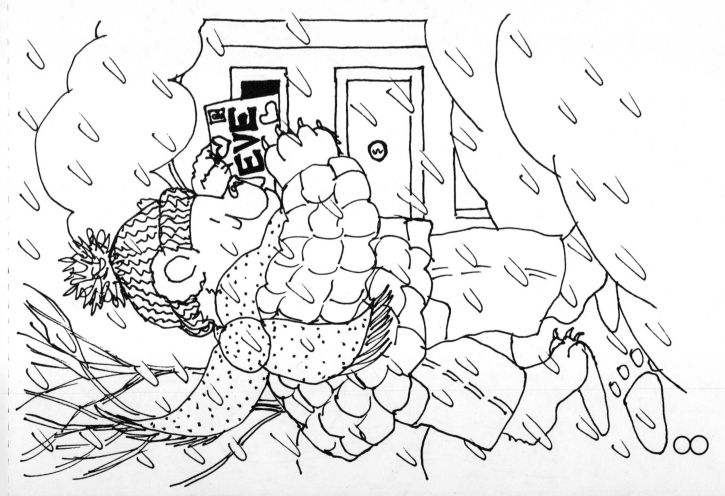

8

Just to let you know . . .

In Open Court's *Collections for Young Scholars*™ reading program, your child has been learning letters and sounds to enable him or her to begin to read independently. Remember to encourage your child to sound out and blend words as you share each Step-by-Step Practice Story. This practice will help your child to become a confident and independent reader.

Step-by-Step Practice Stories 33–36 will focus on the following sounds and spellings:

Story 33 — long *e* spelled *e* (as in *he*) and *e _ e* (as in *these*)

Story 34 — long *e* spelled *ee* (as in *need*)

Story 35 — *qu* (as in *queen*)

Story 36 — long *e* spelled *y* (as in *party*)

Tear off the following activity and post it on your refrigerator where you can refer to it to practice reading with your child.

- -

REFRIGERATOR ACTIVITY

Mystery Word

You need: index cards or scraps of paper

What to do: Write each word from the list below on a separate card or scrap of paper. Place these word cards face up in front of your child. Make up clues about each word, and have your child find and read the correct word card.

Sample clue: I'm thinking of an animal that lives underground. *(mole)*

bike	ice	kite	smile
stone	cold	nose	mole
mule	huge	music	roses

Alfonso is a trader.
He cuts branches,
and trades them at the river.
The branches are used to make
baskets and fish traps.

After Alfonso cuts the branches,
he makes a huge pile.
Then he puts the pile
on Cupid's back.

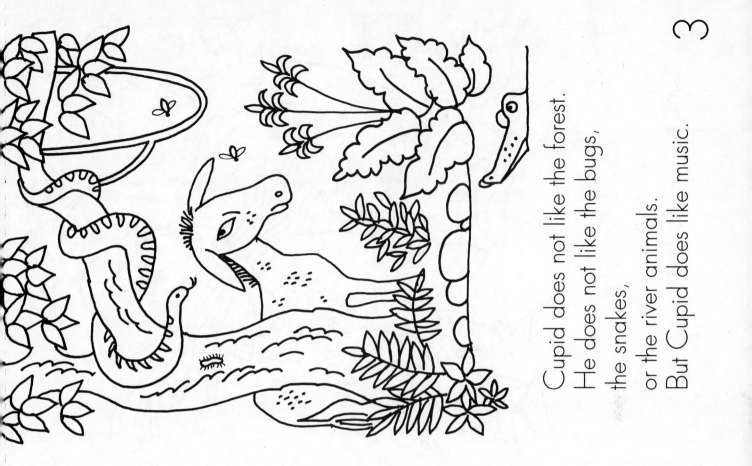

Cupid does not like the forest.
He does not like the bugs,
the snakes,
or the river animals.
But Cupid does like music.

3

Cupid does not like the huge pile.
He refuses to go to the river.
Alfonso pushes and pulls,
but Cupid does not budge.

6

2

Cupid is a mule.
He lives in a forest
close to the Amazon River.

7

At last Alfonso gets out his pipes.
His pipes make fine music.
The music amuses Cupid.

Cupid the Mule

by Dottie Raymer
illustrated by Allen Eitzen

1

Cupid does not like the forest.
He does not like the bugs,
the snakes, or his huge pile.
But Cupid does like music!

8

The Surprise

by Alice Cary
illustrated by Kate Flanagan

8

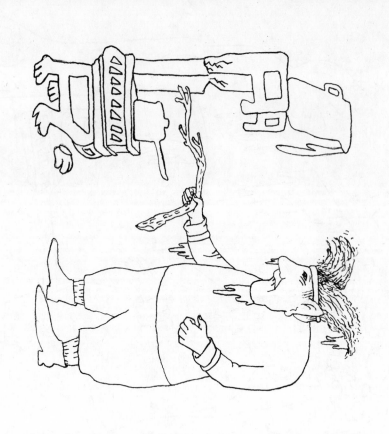

The troll gave his broken stove a poke.
"This is no joke," he said.
"This cold is too much.
I have one last hope. I will go visit Mole."

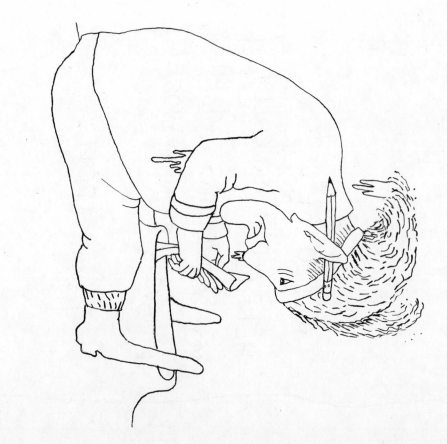

Mole had a nice snug hole.
The cold troll wrote a note.
He slipped the note into Mole's hole.

The old troll's home was cold.
It was so cold that ice was on his nose.
It was so cold that his stove froze.

3

HELLO MOLE!

HELP! I AM SO COLD!

MY STOVE HAS FROZEN.

I HAVE ICE ON MY NOSE!

JAKE TROLL

6

2

Once an old troll had a home
made of stone.

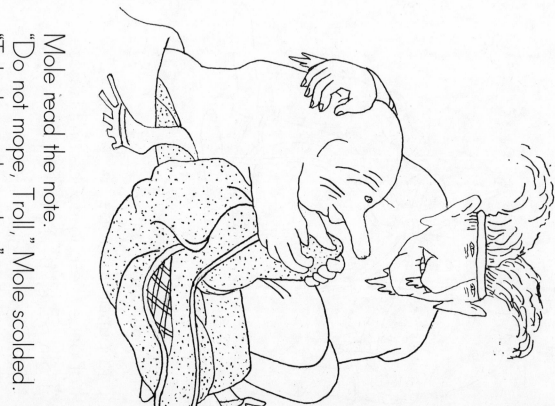

Mole read the note.
"Do not mope, Troll," Mole scolded.
"Take home this robe."

7

The Cold Troll

by Amy Goldman Koss

illustrated by Rosekrans Hoffman

Step-by-Step Practice Story 30 _____

© 1995 Open Court Publishing Company

The troll went home
and put on the robe.
For once, he had no ice on his nose.
"I am not cold!" said the troll.
"Thank you, Mole!"

8

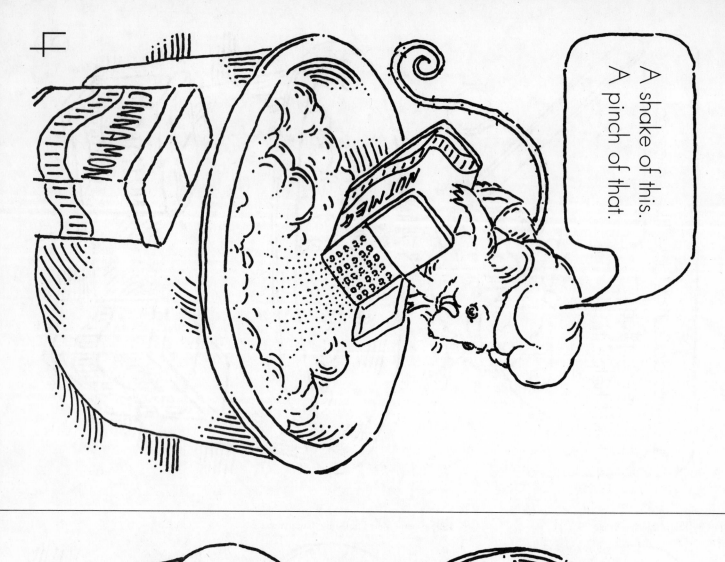

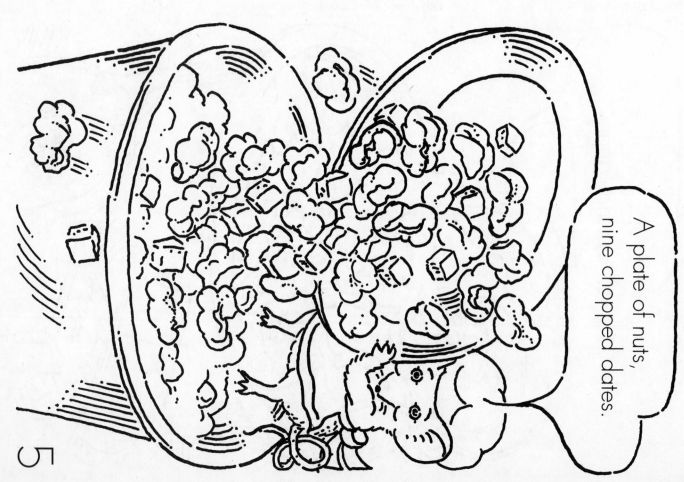

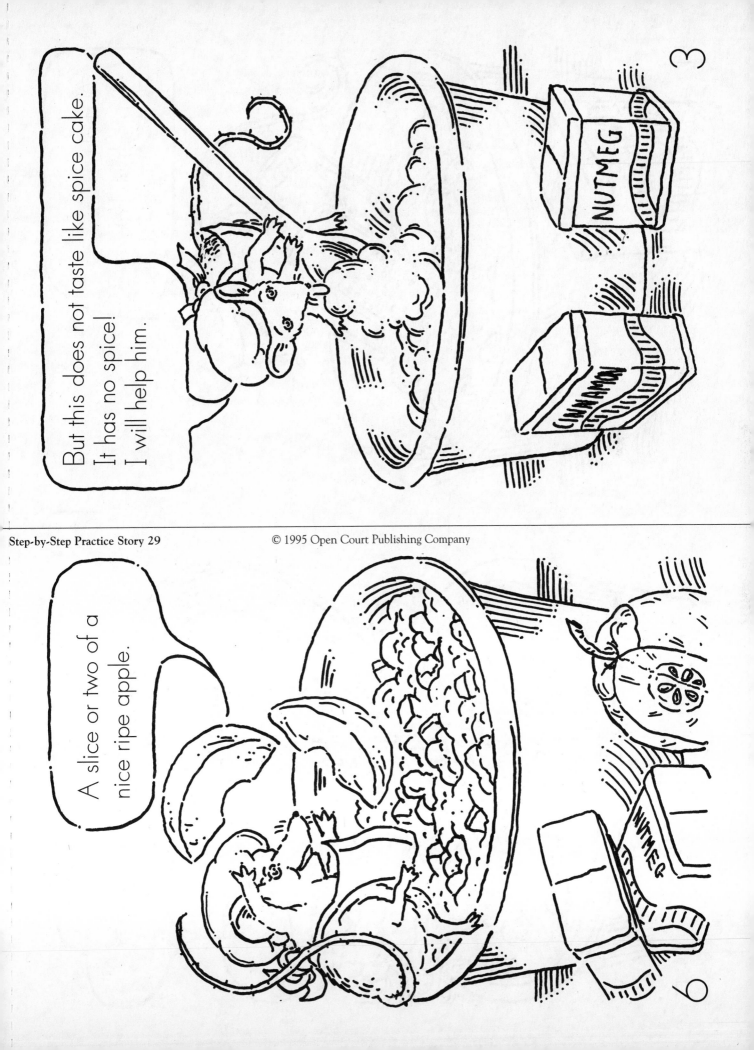

But this does not taste like spice cake.
It has no spice!
I will help him.

NUTMEG

CINNAMON

3

© 1995 Open Court Publishing Company

A slice or two of a nice ripe apple.

NUTMEG

6

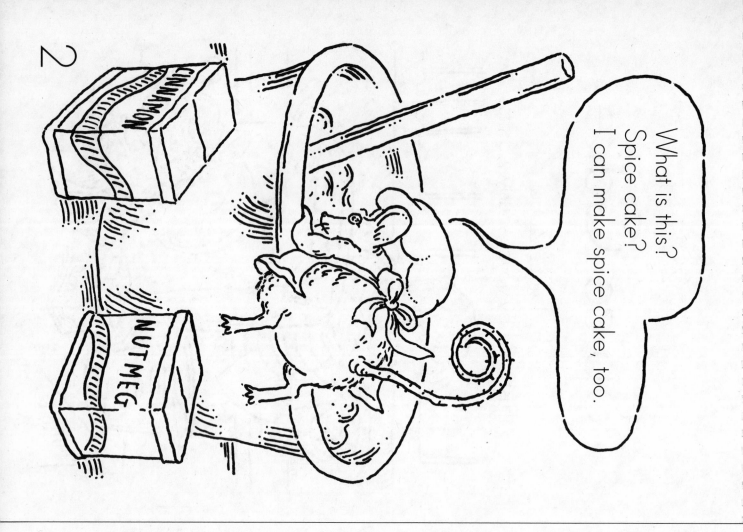

2

What is this?
Spice cake?
I can make spice cake, too.

7

Stir it a while.
And then bake it . . . .

Spice Cake

by Diane Zaga

illustrated by Joyce Audy Zarins

. . . and save a slice for me!

8

Where is Spike?
April finds him.
"Jump in, Spike," she says.
"It is time for the parade!"

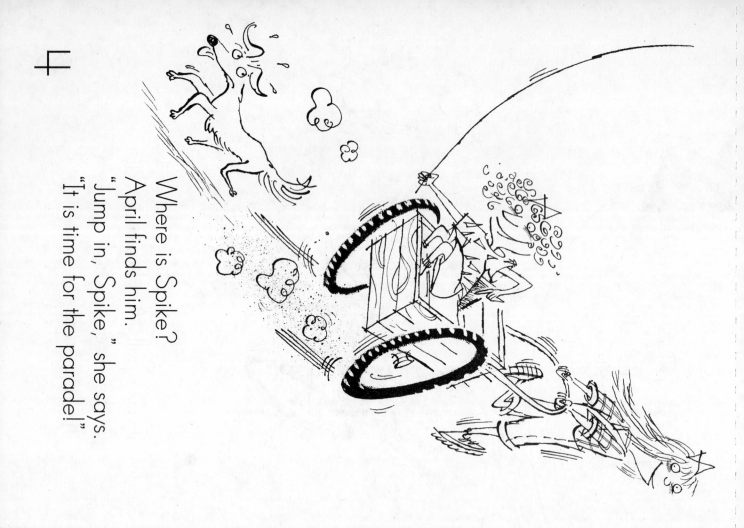

But Spike hates parades.
He hides inside the shed.
He barks and whines.
"Do not mind him," says April.

Nissa pulls April and her kite
in the wagon.
It's a parade!

3

The parade heads up a wide path
and under a white bridge.
"My kite!" yells April.
"Where is my kite?"

6

Tina rides a bike.
Emma rides a trike.
Kamara skates.

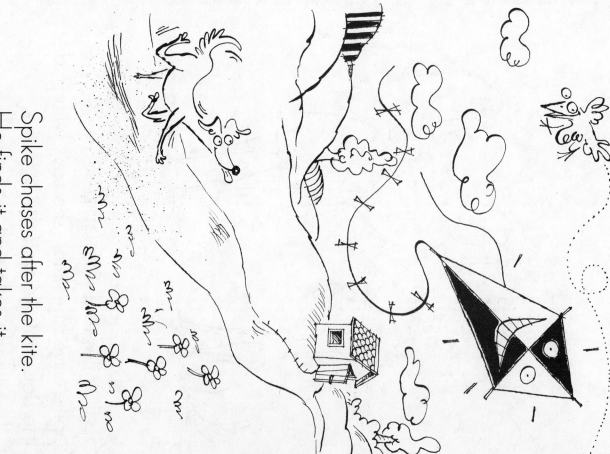

Spike chases after the kite.
He finds it and takes it
back to the shed.

A Fine Parade

by Anne O'Brien

illustrated by Rowan Barnes-Murphy

1

© 1995 Open Court Publishing Company

April smiles and pats Spike.
"Spike saved my kite!" she says with pride.
"He does not like parades.
But he is a fine dog all the same."

8

Just to let you know . . .

Be your child's partner in learning. The value of your child's reading practice increases greatly when it is shared with you. Support your child with interest and enthusiasm about reading. You won't regret it!

Step-by-Step Practice Stories 28–32 will focus on the following letters and sounds:

Story 28 — long *i* spelled *i* (as in *find*) and *i _ e* (as in *ride*)

Story 29 — long *i* spelled *i _ e* (as in *spice*)

Story 30 — long *o* spelled *o* (as in *cold*) and *o _ e* (as in *hole*)

Story 31 — long *o* spelled *o _ e* (as in *rose*)

Story 32 — long *u* spelled *u* (as in *music*) and *u _ e* (as in *mule*)

Tear off the following activity and post it on your refrigerator where you can refer to it to practice reading with your child.

REFRIGERATOR ACTIVITY

Code (or is it cod?) Words

You need: paper and pencil

What to do: Write the words from the list below that are not in parentheses. Ask your child to read each word and discuss what it means. Then have your child add an *e* onto the end of each word to make the words in parentheses. Ask your child to read each new word aloud. Talk about the meaning of each new word.

cap (cape)	hat (hate)	hid (hide)
mad (made)	bit (bite)	dim (dime)
rip (ripe)	tap (tape)	rob (robe)
plan (plane)	scrap (scrape)	hop (hope)

I can wade with sharks,
or jump on the back
of a whale.

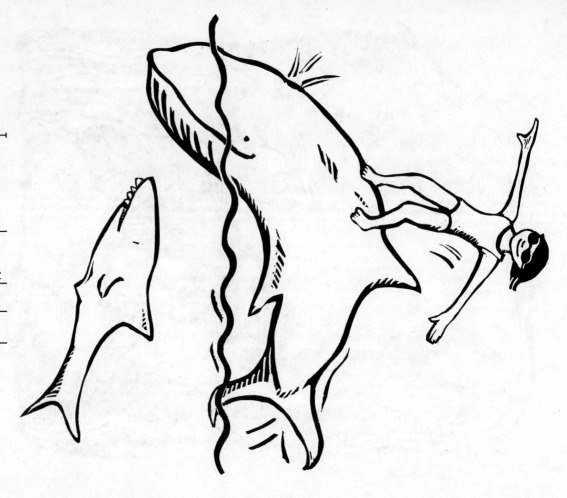

I can catch large snakes,
tame them,
and put them in cages.

. . . to a far land
to hunt for gems.

I can watch camels run
or giraffes graze.

When I turn my magic pages,
I can take a trip . . . .

I can battle blazes
and escape!

Magic Pages

by Anne O'Brien

illustrated by Nelle Davis

1

Turn the page,
and I am back,
safe in my little bed!

8

She hopped a hedge
and jumped up on a bridge.

Jake sat under the bridge.
"Jake!" called Jane. "I have fudge for you!"

Jane put the jar in a pack.
She trudged up to the ridge.
She trudged in the mud.

3

Jane nudged Jake.
She jabbed him with the jar.
"Wake up, Jake! You have a job to do!"

6

Jane baked fudge for Jake.
She put the fudge in a jar
to take to him.

"I am glad that you came, Jane," said Jake.
"I should not nap on the job."

Jane and Jake

by Amy Goldman Koss

illustrated by Rosekrans Hoffman

1

"I am glad I came, too," said Jane.
"I just wish I had a jet to take me back!"

8

Gull and Crane fished together.
Crane waded into the lake.
His shape made shade on the water.
Fish swam into the shade.
That was a mistake!

Snake had a nest across the lake.
He was mad at Crane and Gull.
They ate Snake's fish!
"I can get rid of them," hissed Snake.

Gull and Crane did the same things.
They waded in the same lake.
They ate the same fish.

3

Snake crossed the lake.
He swam into the grass
where Crane napped.

6

Gull and Crane were pals.

But Gull was awake. She called,
"Snake in the lake! Snake in the lake!
Watch the shade where you wade!"

Gull and Crane

by Helen Byers

illustrated by Jean and Mou-sien Tseng

1

© 1995 Open Court Publishing Company

"Hurray! They have left!" hissed Snake.
But Snake still had no fish.

8

Just to let you know . . .

Successful reading experiences allow children to be proud of their new-found reading ability. Read and reread Step-by-Step Practice Stories with your child, and give your child a chance to take pride in successful reading.

Step-by-Step Practice Stories 25–27 will focus on the following letters and sounds:

Story 25 — long *a* spelled *a _ e* (as in *snake*)

Story 26 — *j, dge* (as in *judge*)

Story 27 — long *a* spelled *a _ e* (as in *page*)

Tear off the following activity and post it on your refrigerator where you can refer to it to practice reading with your child.

REFRIGERATOR ACTIVITY

Story Swap

What to do: Have your child choose a favorite character from one of the Step-by-Step Practice Stories you have read together. With your child, create a new story about the character. Take turns telling one sentence at a time, for example:

Child:	Mitch liked to collect trash.
You:	One day, Mitch found a rusty, old chest.
Child:	The chest was locked, and Mitch couldn't open it.
You:	But Mitch was so curious, he had to get it open!

You may want to have your child draw a picture of a favorite part of the new story.

three chipped dishes,
a bit of a ship,

four strips of fishnet,
a scrap of flag,

a split log,
two smashed beds,

Step-by-Step Practice Story 24 © 1995 Open Court Publishing Company

five lunch boxes,
a bent drum set,
and half a sled.

Mitch had a stash of trash:
one dented bench,

Mitch put his stash of trash
in his garden.

The Trash Stash

by Amy Goldman Koss
illustrated by Susie Stevenson

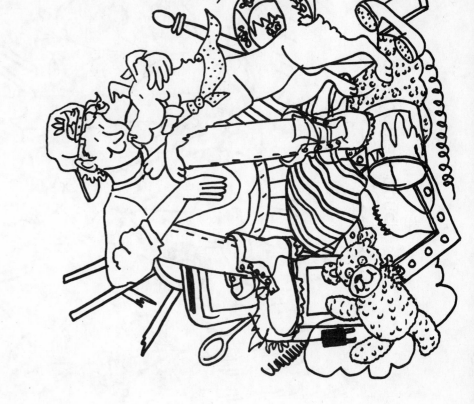

1

Then he called all the children
and said, "Have fun!"

8

"Let's switch," said Chuck.
Chuck was the pitcher.
Lil was the hitter.
Elena was the catcher.
Lil hit the ball hard.
"I'll catch it!" called Chuck.

But the ball went too far,
past Chuck,
past the grass,
past the bushes,
into the ditch.

5

Elena pitched the ball
and Lil hit it.
Elena ran after the ball
and tossed it to Chuck.

3

"Here Patch!" Elena called to her dog.
"Fetch the ball, Patch!"

6

Lil, Elena, and Chuck met at the ball park.
Elena said, "I will be the pitcher.
You be the hitter, Lil.
Chuck, you can be the catcher."

2

Patch ran past Chuck.
He ran past the grass.
He ran past the bushes
and into the ditch.
He fetched the ball.

7

Step-by-Step 23 Practice Story

Patch Gets the Ball

by Anne O'Brien

illustrated by Andy San Diego

"Smart dog, Patch," said Elena.
"Let's do this.
Chuck can be the hitter.
I will be the pitcher.
Lil can be the catcher,
and Patch can be the fetcher!"

8

"Monster fish in the water!
Man the masts!"

"We have hit the rocks!
Get the rafts!"

"Cast off!" called Seth.
"All hands on deck!"

3

"The ship is under water!
Abandon ship!"

6

2

Seth stepped into the bath water.
"To the ship!" he yelled.

7

Seth's Bath

by Anne O'Brien

illustrated by Joyce Audy Zarins

"All finished, Seth?" said Dad.

"Yes, Dad," said Seth. "All finished!"

8

4

5

Jen spins her web.
What is it for?

But it is for a bug!

Step-by-Step 2 | Practice Story

Jen's Web

by Marilyn Jager Adams
illustrated by Nadine Westcott

Help! I am stuck!
This is a mess for me!

8

Just to let you know . . .

Have you read a good book today? Children who read every day come to think of reading as a pleasant, natural part of life. One way to inspire your child to read is to show that reading is an important part of your life by letting him or her see you reading books, magazines, newspapers, or any other materials. Another good way to show that you value reading is to share a Step-by-Step Practice Story with your child each day.

Step-by-Step Practice Stories 21–24 will focus on the following letters and sounds:

Story 21 — short vowels (as in *bat, web, fish, not, bug*)

Story 22 — *sh, th* (as in *show, bath*)

Story 23 — *ch, tch* (as in *chair, catch*)

Story 24 — clusters of consonants (as the *scr* in *scrap*)

Tear off the following activity and post it on your refrigerator where you can refer to it to practice reading with your child.

REFRIGERATOR ACTIVITY

Elephant Word Hunt

You need: pencil and paper

What to do: Write the word *elephant* at the top of a piece of paper. Ask your child how many three-letter words he or she can make from the letters in the word *elephant.* You may want to use one of the following as an example: *hat, hen, lap, let, nap, pal, pan.*

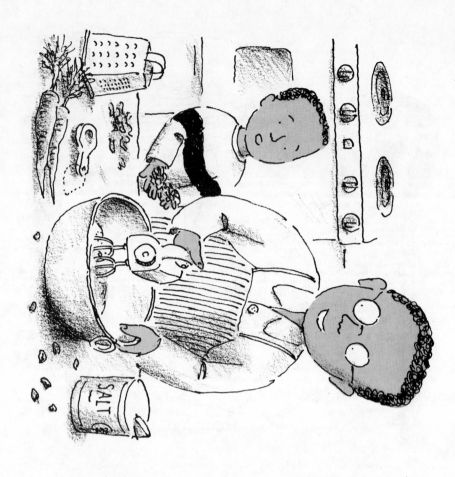

Uncle Art put the eggs and salt
into the mixer.
WHIR!
"What is it?" wondered Bert.
"Hand me the carrots, Bert,"
said Uncle Art.
"We will stir in the nuts, too."

Uncle Art put the carrots and nuts
into the mixer.
WHIR!
"What is it?" wondered Bert.
"Hand me the pan, Bert," said Uncle Art.
"We can put the batter in it."

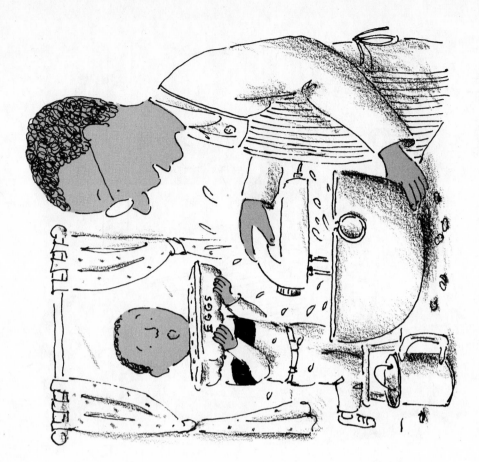

Uncle Art put the butter and milk
into the mixer.
WHIR!
"What is it?" wondered Bert.
"Hand me the eggs, Bert," Uncle Art said.
" and we will stir in a little salt."

3

"What is it?" wondered Bert.
"What is this wonderful smell?"

6

Uncle Art picked up the mixer.
"Hand me the butter, Bert,"
said Uncle Art,
"and we will stir in the milk."

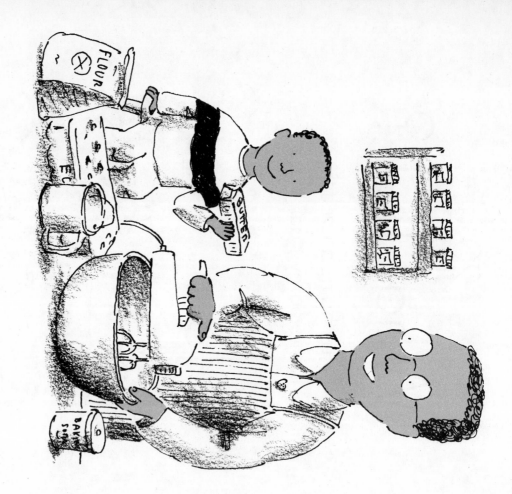

"It was eggs and butter
and milk and carrots.
What did it turn into, Uncle Art?"

What Is It?

by Patricia Griffith
illustrated by Paul Meisel

1

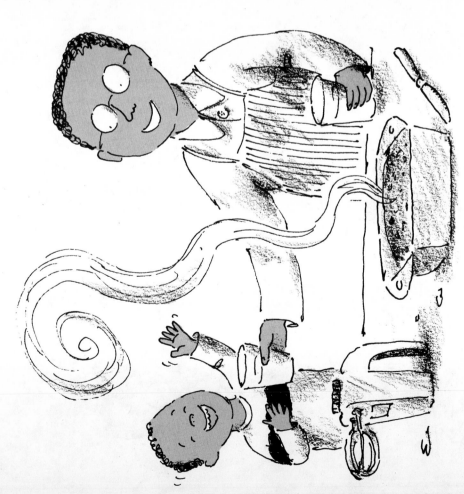

"It turned into carrot bread,"
said Uncle Art.
"Carrot bread! Hurray!" yelled Bert.
"Have a glass of milk, Bert,"
said Uncle Art.

8

T. Rex wants a snack.
"No problem!" says Tess.
"A big salad should fill you up."

Greg's neck is stiff.
"No problem!" says Tess.
"A scarf should do the trick."

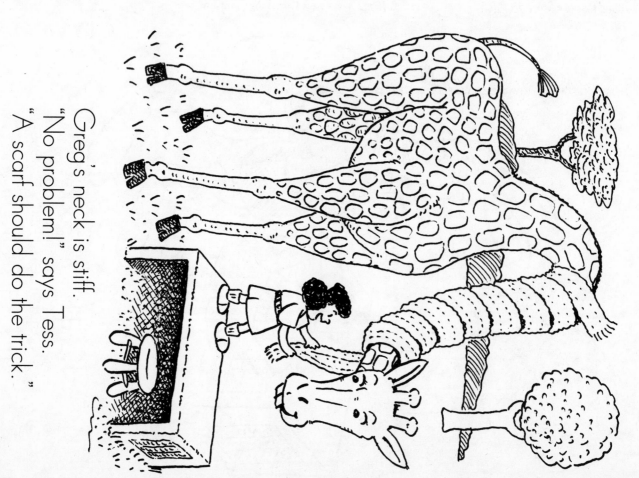

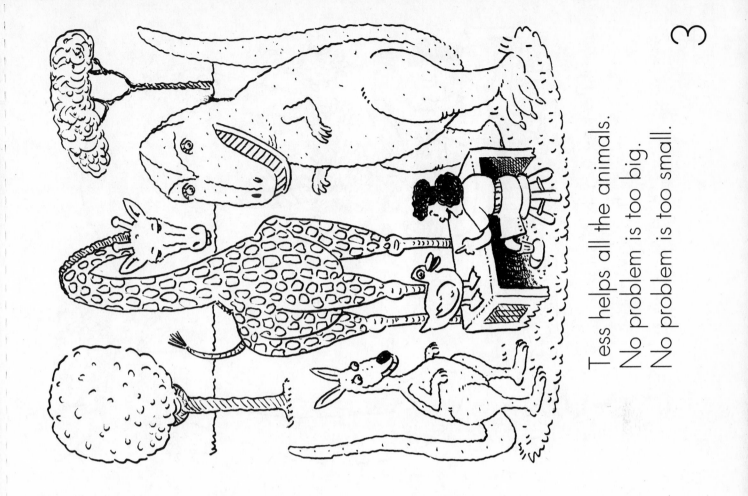

Tess helps all the animals.
No problem is too big.
No problem is too small.

3

Kana has no pocket.
"No problem!" says Tess.
"This belt should fit you."

6

Step up! Step up!
Tess has a stand!
Tess can help!

Deb can't paddle in the pond.
"No problem!" says Tess.
"Rent a raft."

The Stand

by Alice Cary

illustrated by Slug Signorino

1

Tess must step out.
She has to rest.
"No problem!" says Tess.
"No problem at all!"

8

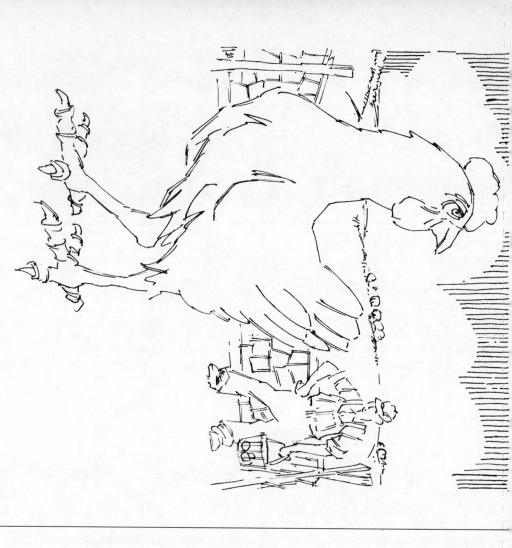

"I'm fed up!" Henetta sniffed.
"Ted says he should mend my pen,
but he still does not mend it."

"I've had it!" Henetta said to the animals.
Henetta ducked her head
and flapped out of the pen.

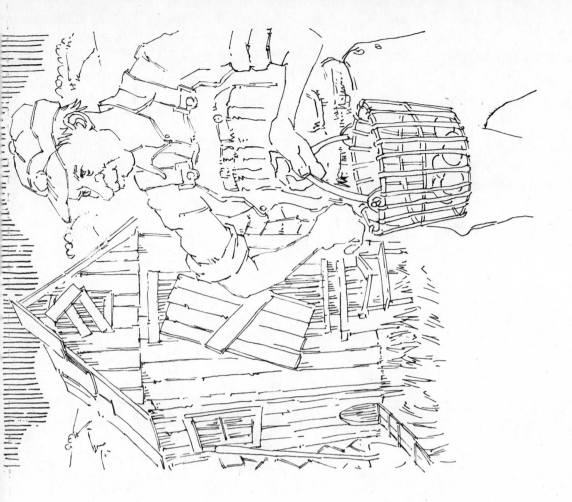

Ted said he would mend
Henetta's pen.
"I should mend it," Ted said.

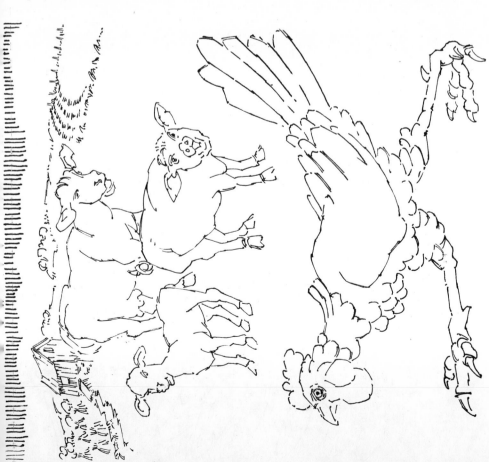

"Hen on the run!" called the animals
as Henetta flapped past.
"Hen on the run!" called Ted.

6

Ted had a hen in a pen.
The hen was Henetta.
Henetta's pen was a mess.
It was small and dented.

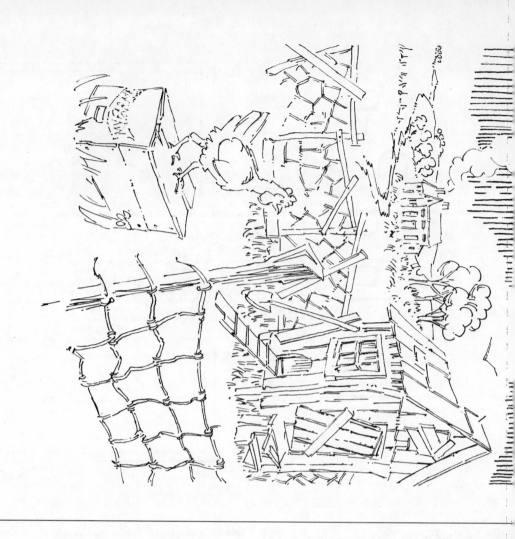

Henetta flapped to the top of the pen.
But she flapped too hard
and fell into a bucket.
"Hen in a bucket!" called the animals.

Hen in a Pen

Step-by-Step 18 Practice Story

by Amy Goldman Koss

illustrated by John Fulweiler

Ted pulled his hen out of the bucket.
He petted her head and fed her.
"I should mend this pen!" Ted said.
And he did.

8

Meg pulled and pulled.
She passed a bulldog.
"Bulldog," said Meg,
"help me pull this sled."
"I can't," said the bulldog.
"My neck would get damp."

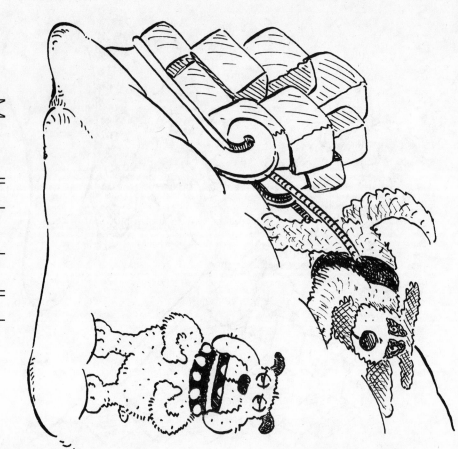

Meg got to the top.
She unpacked the sled.
She stepped onto the sled.
Away she sped.

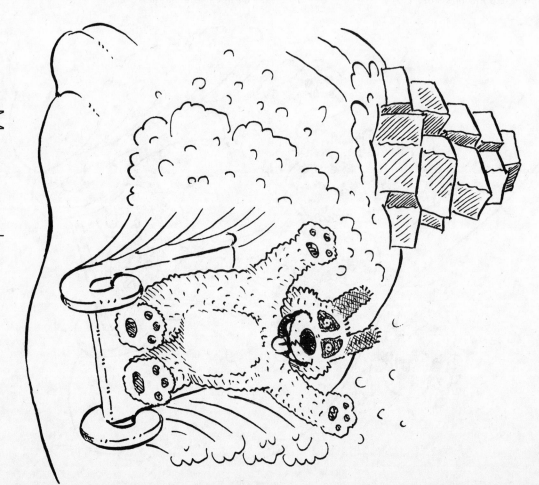

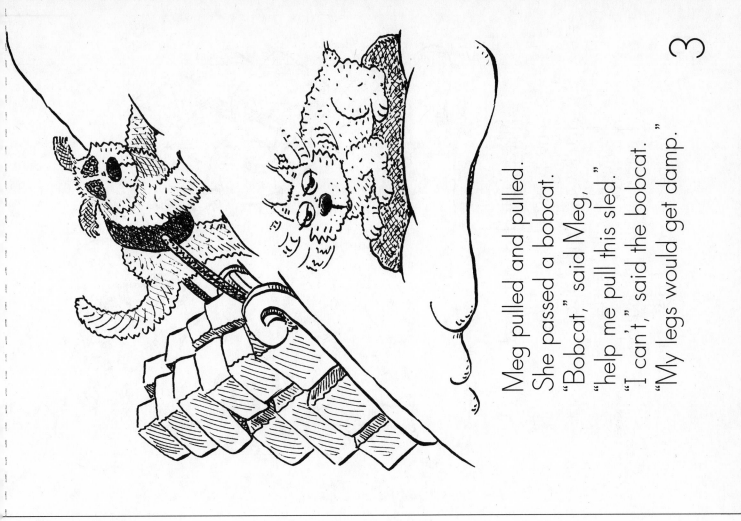

Meg pulled and pulled.
She passed a bobcat.
"Bobcat," said Meg,
"help me pull this sled."
"I can't," said the bobcat.
"My legs would get damp."

3

© 1995 Open Court Publishing Company

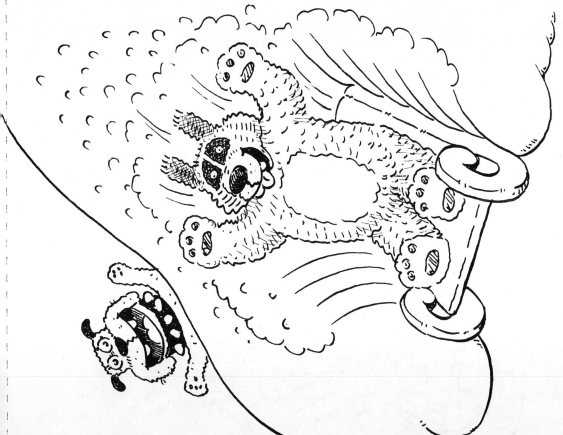

Meg sped past the bulldog.
"Meg!" said the bulldog. "Let me hop on!"

6

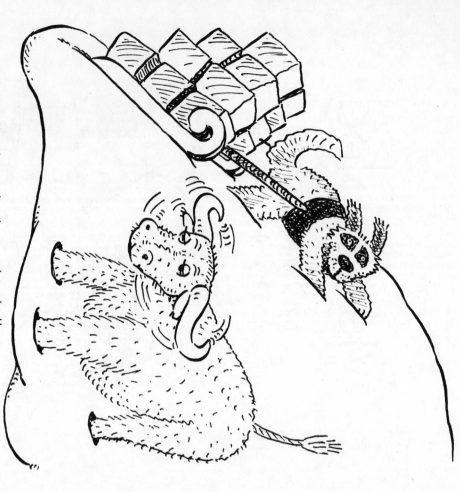

Meg pulled a sled up the hill.
She passed an ox.
"Ox," said Meg, "help me pull this sled."
"I can't," said the ox.
"My back would get damp."

2

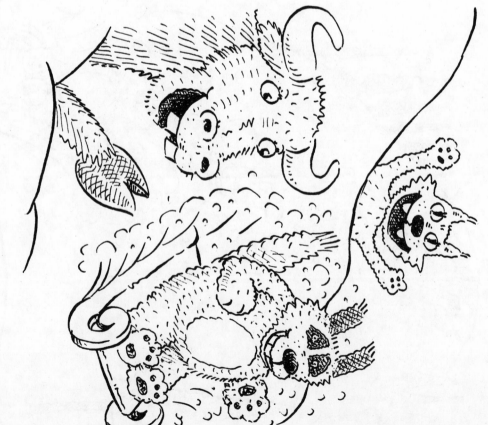

Meg sped past the bobcat.
"Meg!" said the bobcat. "Let me hop on!"
Meg sped past the ox.
"Meg!" said the ox. "Let me hop on!"

7

Meg's Sled

by Dottie Raymer

illustrated by Slug Signorino

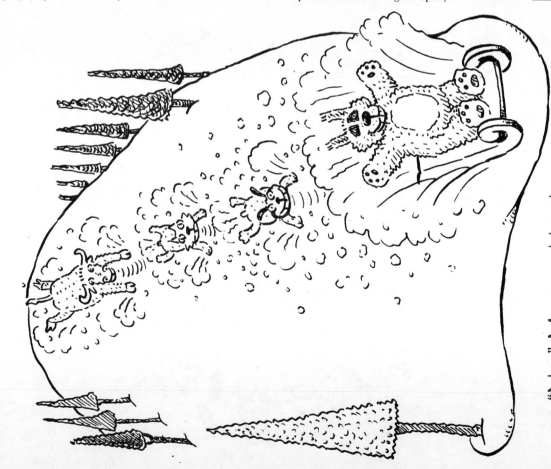

"No," Meg said back.
"You would all get too damp!"
And Meg and the sled sped on.

8

Just to let you know . . .

Learning to read takes lots of practice. Sharing Step-by-Step Practice Stories is one way that your child can gain that valuable practice. Remember to read and reread the Step-by-Step Practice Stories collected in your child's home library.

Step-by-Step Practice Stories 17–20 will focus on the following letters and sounds:

Story 17 — short *e* (as in *sled*)

Story 18 — short *e*

Story 19 — short *e*

Story 20 — *er, ir, ur* (as in *her, stir, turn*)

Tear off the following activity and post it on your refrigerator where you can refer to it to practice reading with your child.

REFRIGERATOR ACTIVITY

Word Tic-Tac-Toe

You need: scrap paper and a pencil

What to do: Have your child draw a tic-tac-toe grid on a sheet of paper. In each square, have her or him write one word from the following list of words from Step-by-Step Practice Stories 1–16. Call out words from the list in any order and tell your child to put an *X* over the word when you say it. Play until your child gets "Tic-Tac-Toe, three in a row!" Encourage other family members to play, with each person taking a turn as the caller.

is	on	the	in	was
are	has	have	here	he
you	no	but	says	too
this	said	yes	of	for

4

The man on the bus said,
"I am Zack the One-Man Band,
and here is my big brass band!"

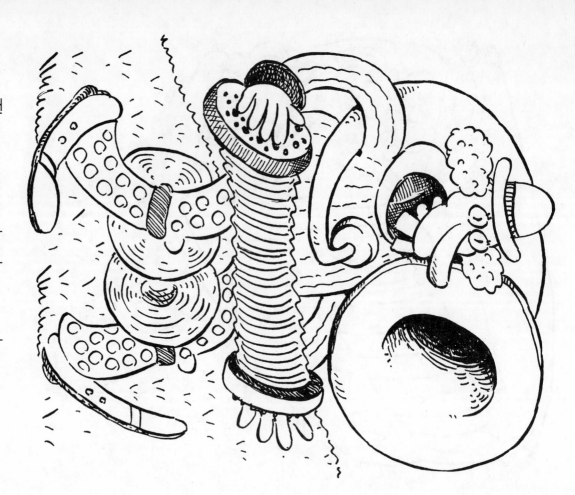

"Sit here on the grass.
You can hum. You can tap.
You can drum and snap."

5

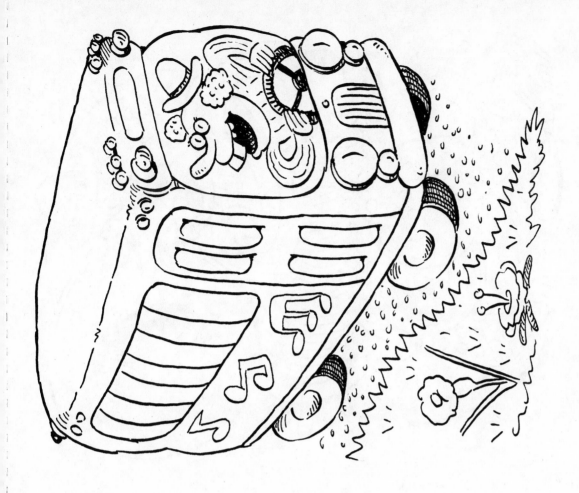

"It's a bus," said Gus.
"It's a bus and a man
and a big brass band!"

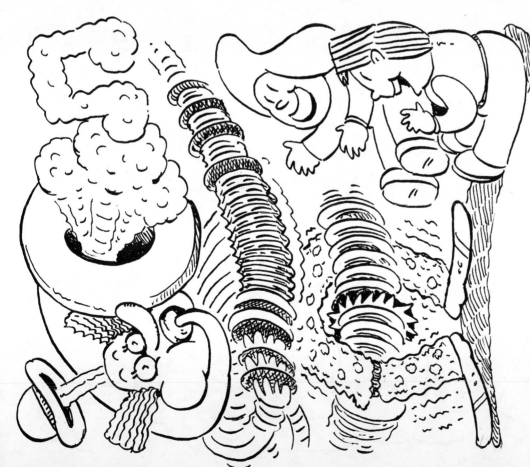

BAM! BUZZ! BOP!
The band started up.
"Zack, you are grand!" said Cass.
"What a band!"

Gus and Cass sat on a rock.
ZAP! POP! SNAP!
"What is it?" said Cass.
"What is the fuss?"

Zack huffed and puffed.
"I must stop," he said.

Zack the One-Man Band

by Diane Zaga
illustrated by Slug Signorino

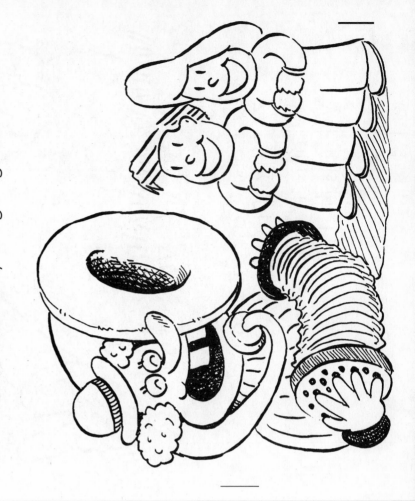

© 1995 Open Court Publishing Company

"Do not fuss," said Zack.
"Grab a pot! Grab a stick!
Start a band!" he said.
And Zack the One-Man Band
got back on his bus.

8

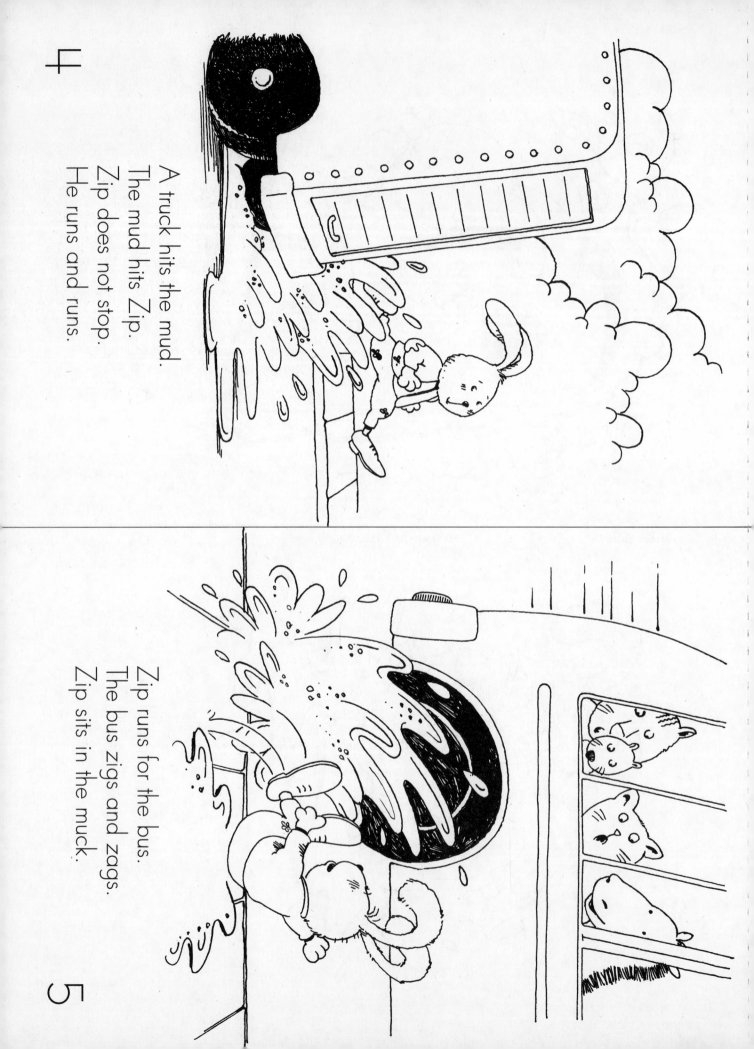

4

A truck hits the mud.
The mud hits Zip.
Zip does not stop.
He runs and runs.

5

Zip runs for the bus.
The bus zigs and zags.
Zip sits in the muck.

A cup and a bun,
and Zip is back on the run.

3

Stuck in the muck!
This run was no fun.

6

Zip mops and dusts his hut.
He hums as he runs. It's fun!

2

The bus runs on,
but Zip does not run.

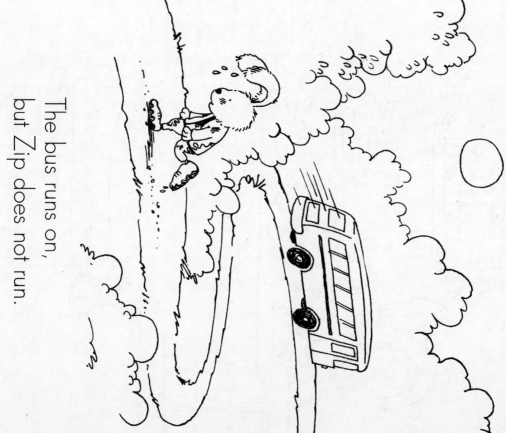

7

Step-by-Step | 15 | Practice Story

Zip on the Run

by Alice Cary

illustrated by Paige Billin-Frye

The sun is up.
Zip is on the run.

1

Zip sits in a tub of suds.

8

Step-by-Step Practice Story 14   © 1995 Open Court Publishing Company

2

7

The Bug

by Janet Klausner

illustrated by Jack Wallen

1

I am not big!

8

Just to let you know . . .

Take a reading break! It only takes a few minutes to share a Step-by-Step Practice Story with your child. Your child will gain important reading practice, and both of you will enjoy a moment of togetherness at the end of a busy day.

Step-by-Step Practice Stories 14–16 will focus on the following letters and sounds:

Story 14 — short *u* (as in *bug*)

Story 15 — short *u* (as in *gum*)

Story 16 — final *zz, ss, ff* (as in *buzz, fuss, puff*)

Tear off the following activity and post it on your refrigerator where you can refer to it to practice reading with your child.

REFRIGERATOR ACTIVITY

Treasure Hunt

You need: Step-by-Step Practice Story books

What to do: Choose a word from a Step-by-Step Practice Story that you and your child have read together. Have your child find and count how many times the word appears in the story. Compare your child's tally with your own.

I picked a spot.
I fixed my bag.

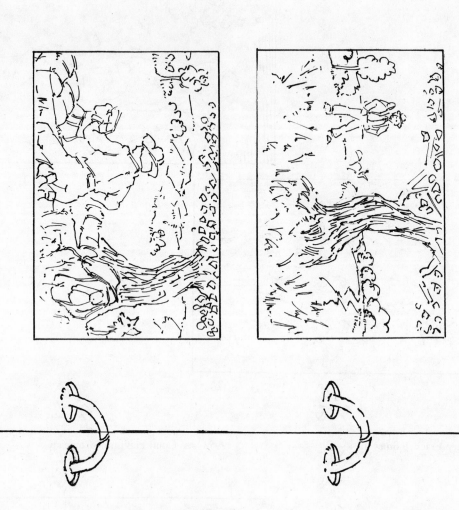

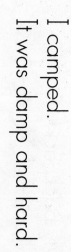

I camped.
It was damp and hard.

I sat on a rock.
I had a snack.

Step-by-Step Practice Story 13

My backpack!
No picnic! No snack!

For my trip, I packed a backpack.
I had a map.
I tramped and stamped.

I tracked a fox.
My picnic!

My Trip

by Alice Cary

illustrated by John Fulweiler

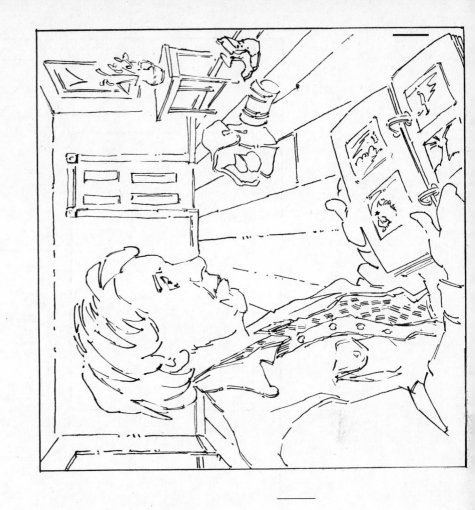

I camped and tramped.
But the fox had a picnic!

8

"You sit here, Max," said Mom.
"You can have a star here."

Max said, "Stars are far away.
I can't have a star here."

"Mom, can I have a star?" said Max.
"Hmmm . . . a star . . . ," said Mom.

3

© 1995 Open Court Publishing Company

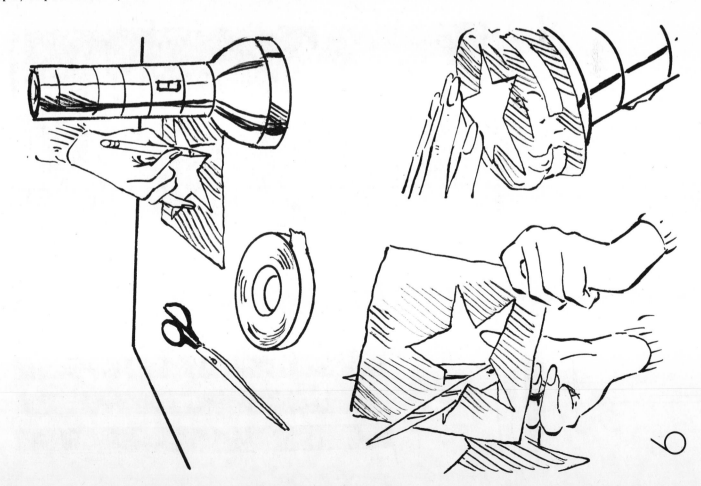

6

"Mom, are stars far away?" said Max.
"Yes, Max," said Mom.
"Stars are far, far away."

"Here, Max," said Mom.
"Here is a star for you."

Grab a Star

by Dottie Raymer
illustrated by Gavin Curtis

"I have a star!" said Max.
"Mom, you are smart!"

8

"Can it trap a cat?" said Rabbit.
"Yes," said Fox. "It can trap a cat."

"Can it trap a hog?" said Rabbit.
"Yes," said Fox. "It can trap a hog."

"Can it trap a frog?" said Rabbit.
"Yes," said Fox. "It can trap a frog."

3

"Can it trap an ox?" said Rabbit.
"Not an ox," said Fox, "but it can trap a rabbit."

6

"You have a big box," said Rabbit.
"Yes," said Fox. "It is a trap."

"It can trap a rabbit?" said Rabbit.
"But I am a rabbit!"

1

A Fox and His Box

by Marj Milano

illustrated by Kate Flanagan

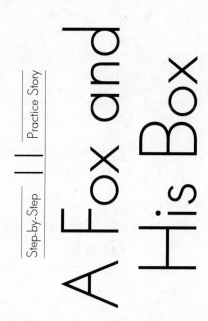
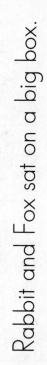

Rabbit and Fox sat on a big box.

"Yes," said Fox,
"but it did not trap you!"

8

This is Hog.
Hog has a cot.

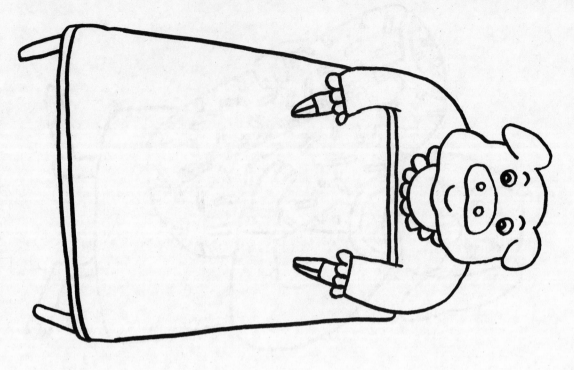

Frog hops on the cot.

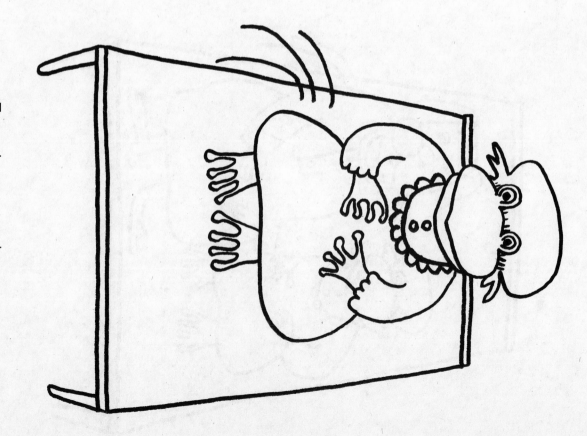

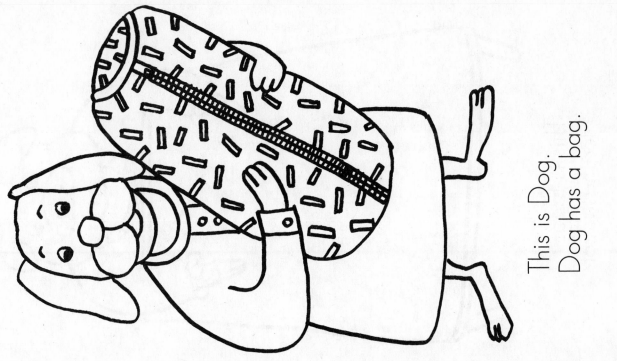

This is Dog.
Dog has a bag.

© 1995 Open Court Publishing Company

Dog hops on the cot.

This is Frog.
Frog has a cap.

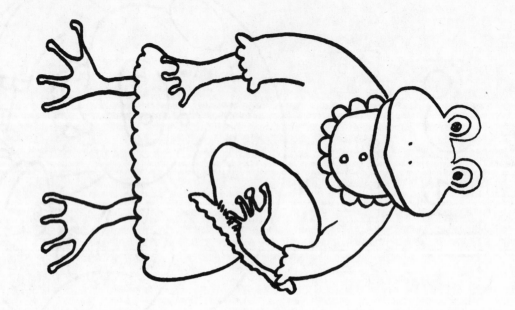

Hog hops on the cot.
OOPS!

Step-by-Step 10 Practice Story

The Cot

by Marilyn Jager Adams
illustrated by Oki Han

© 1995 Open Court Publishing Company

Just to let you know . . .

Encourage your child to keep the Step-by-Step Practice Stories in a special place. This collection will make a library of books that your child can read and reread. Take the time to listen to your child read from his or her library. Just a few moments of shared reading each day can give your child the confidence needed to excel in reading.

Step-by-Step Practice Stories 10–13 will focus on the following letters and sounds:

Story 10 — short *o* (as in *dog*)

Story 11 — *x* (as in *fox*)

Story 12 — *ar* (as in *star*)

Story 13 — *ck* and the past-tense word ending *-ed* (as in *packed*)

Tear off the following activity and post it on your refrigerator where you can refer to it to practice reading with your child.

- -

REFRIGERATOR ACTIVITY

Rhyming Relay

What to do: Call out a short word with either the short *a* or the short *i* sound, such as *man* or *bit*. Have your child say a word that rhymes with your word. Take turns saying rhyming words (such as *man, fan, tan, ran, can*).

I have big hands.
I can dig fast!

You brag, Fran.
I am as fast as you are!

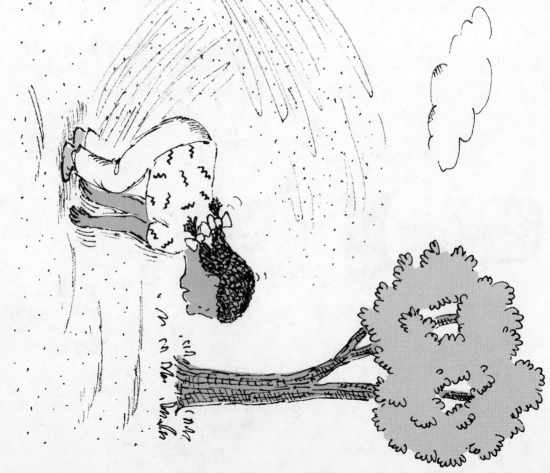

The Sand Pits

Step-by-Step 9 Practice Story

by Amy Goldman Koss
illustrated by Paul Meisel

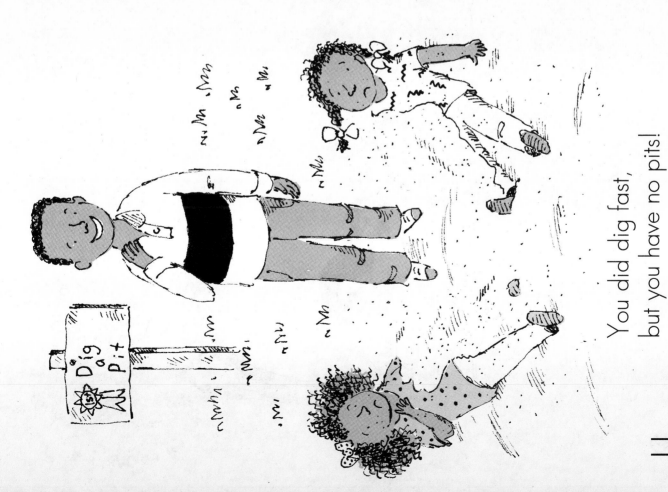

You stand here, Fran.
You stand here, Ann.

You did dig fast,
but you have no pits!

4

Brad's ram spins
and nabs the hat.
Brad is mad.
HE nabs the hat.

Snap! The hat!

Step-by-Step 8 Practice Story

Brad's Ram

by Amy Goldman Koss
illustrated by Sylvie Wickstrom

Brad is a trim man.
He has a trim hat.
He has a fat ram.

1

Brad is a trim man.
He has a fat ram.
The ram has a fat hat!

4

Tim dips.

Tim tips his hat.

Tim Spins

by Anne O'Brien

illustrated by Joyce Audy Zarins

Tim spins.

1

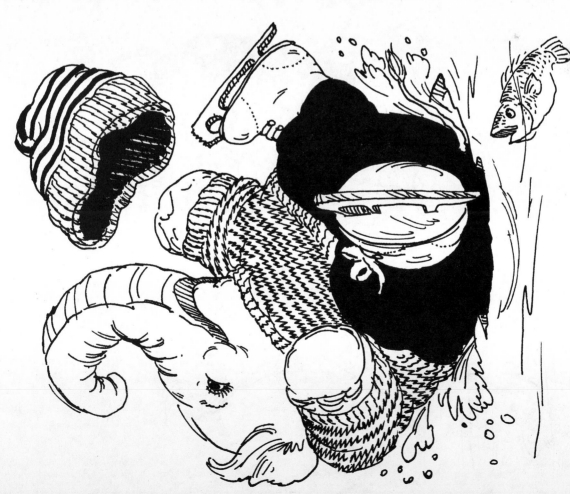

Tim hits a pit . . . .
and sits.

4

I am Sid.
I have a tin can.

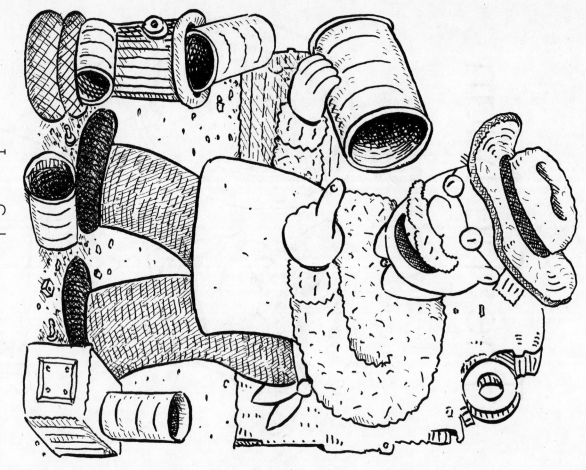

I am Sid.
I have a tin rim.

The Tin Man

by Amy Goldman Koss
illustrated by Slug Signorino

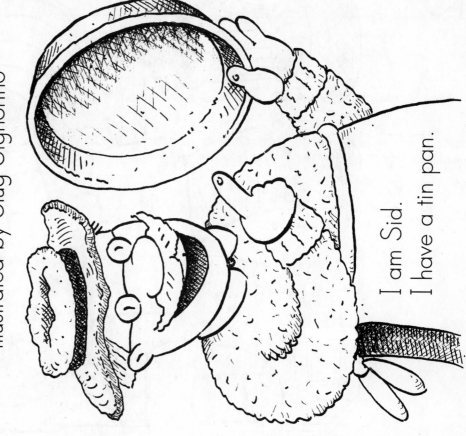

I am Sid.
I have a tin pan.

1

Sid has a tin pan,
Sid has a tin can,
Sid has a tin rim.
Sid has a tin man!

4

Just to let you know . . .

Help your child discover the joy of independent reading! Open Court's Step-by-Step Practice Stories contain only familiar words and the letters and sounds that have been introduced in your child's reading lessons. If your child has difficulty reading a word, ask him or her to say the sounds of the letters and blend the sounds together. Your child may not read the words perfectly. That's fine. Just give lots of encouragement and make reading together fun.

Step-by-Step Practice Stories 6–9 will focus on the following letters and sounds:

Story 6 — short *i* (as in *tin*)

Story 7 — short *i* (as in *Tim*)

Story 8 — short *a* and *i* (as in *ram* and *spin*)

Story 9 — short *a* and *i* (as in *sand* and *pit*)

Tear off the following activity and post it on your refrigerator where you can refer to it to practice reading with your child.

REFRIGERATOR ACTIVITY

I Spy

What to do: Choose an object in the room that begins with a certain letter sound, such as *table* for the sound of letter *t*. Say to your child, "I spy something that begins with the sound *t-t-t-t-t*." Have your child guess the name of the object. Take turns choosing objects and guessing their names.

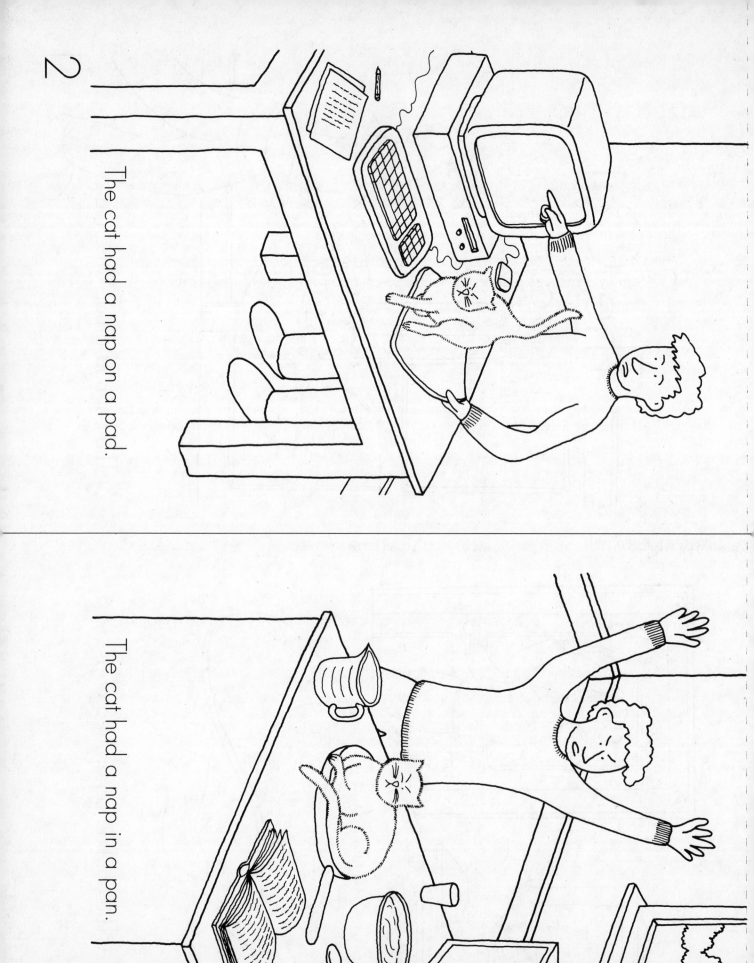

The cat had a nap on a pad.

The cat had a nap in a pan.

The Cat

by Amy Goldman Koss

illustrated by David Neuhaus

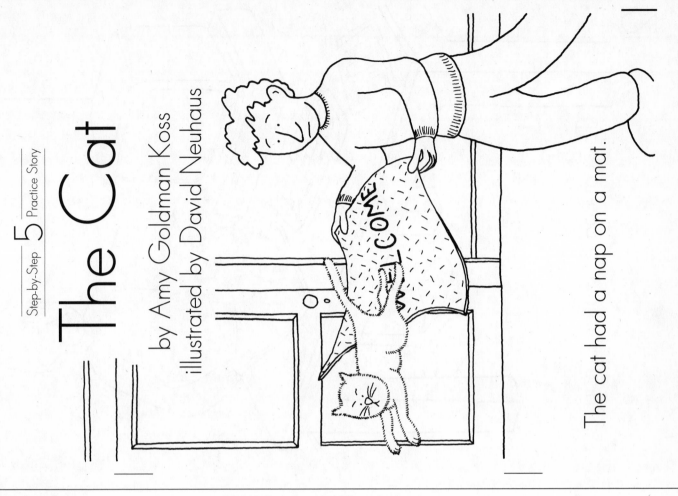

The cat had a nap on a mat.

1

© 1995 Open Court Publishing Company

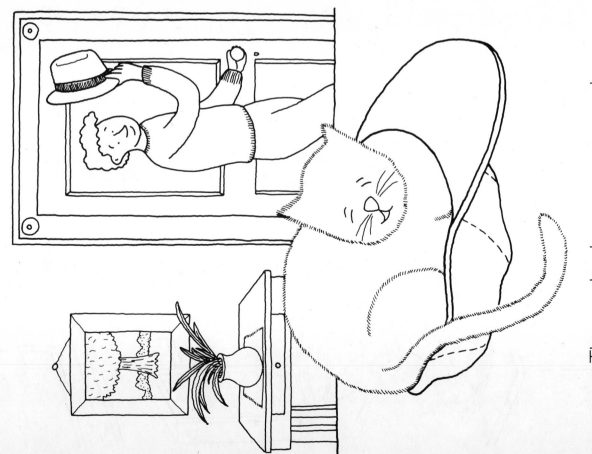

The cat had a nap in a cap!

4

4

Pam has a nap.

The man has a nap.

5

Step-by-Step Practice Story 4   © 1995 Open Court Publishing Company

Pam has a hat.

The man has a hat.

2

Tap! Tap! Tap!

Tap! Tap! Tap!

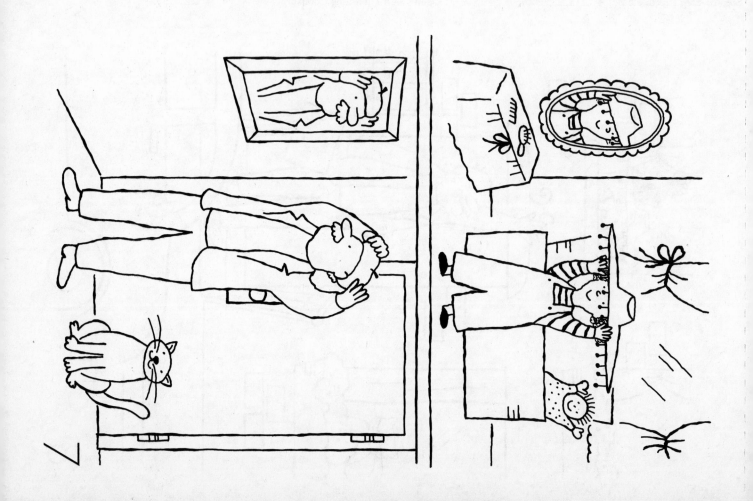

7

Step-by-Step 4 Practice Story

Pam and the Man

by Dottie Raymer

illustrated by Ellen Joy Sasaki

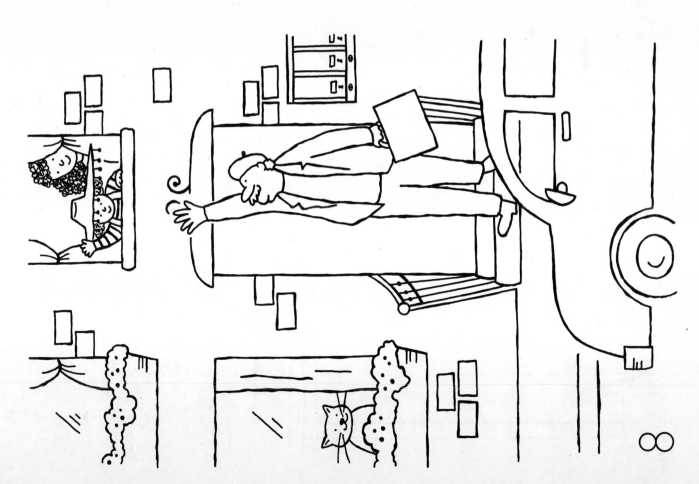

8

In the hat is a

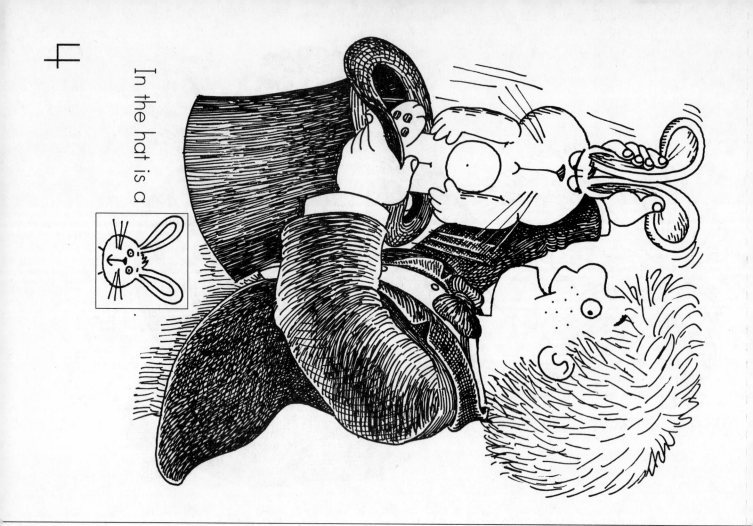

In the hat is a

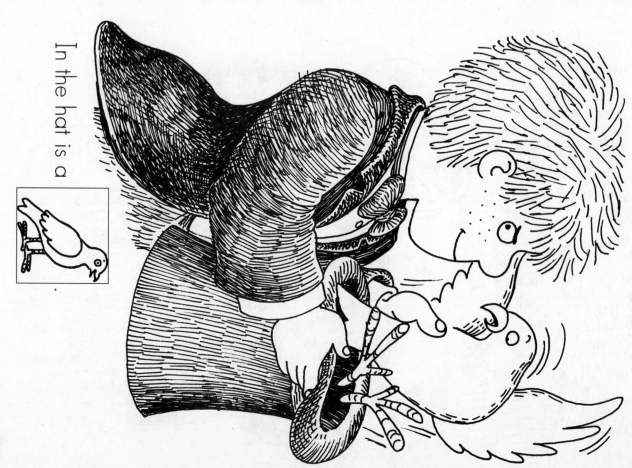

Matt has a hat.

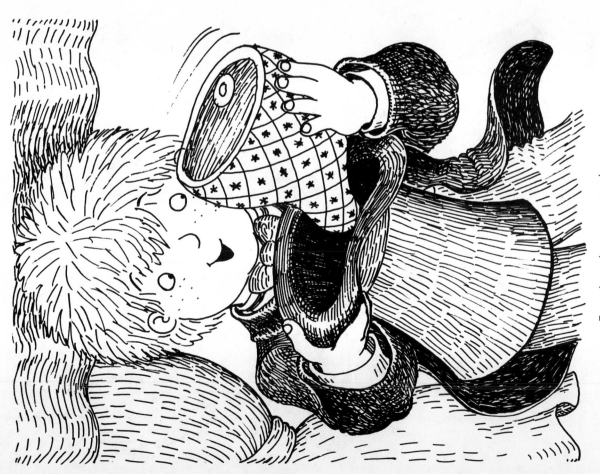

In the hat is a ham.

Matt.

A ham in a hat?

Step-by-Step 3 Practice Story

The Hat

by Amy Goldman Koss
illustrated by Roz Schanzer

A ham!

8

4

On the 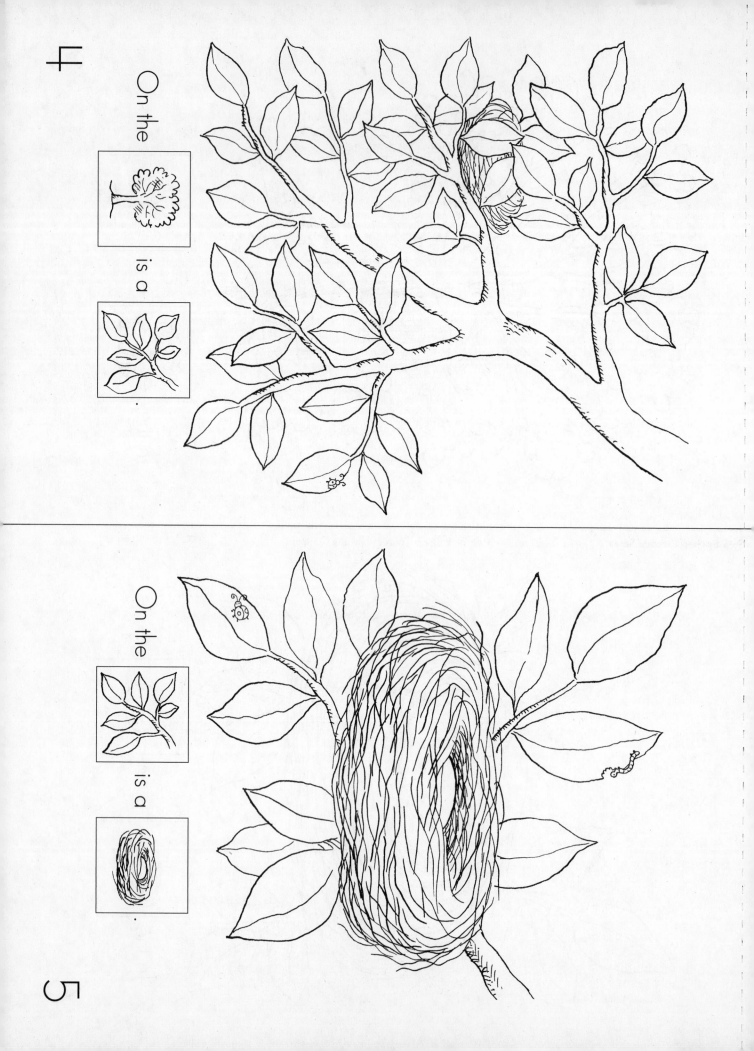 is a
.

On the is a
.

5

In the 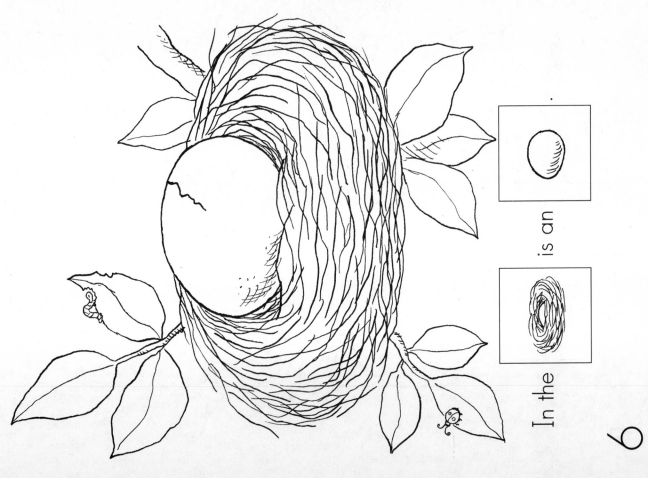 is a .

© 1995 Open Court Publishing Company

In the is an .

On an 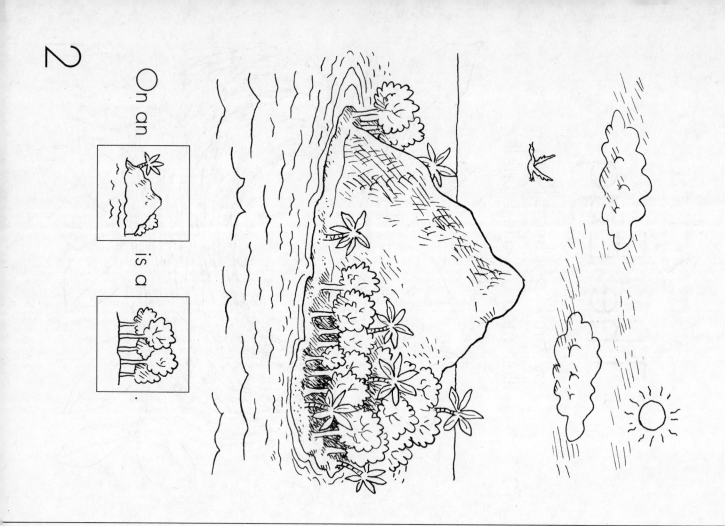 is a 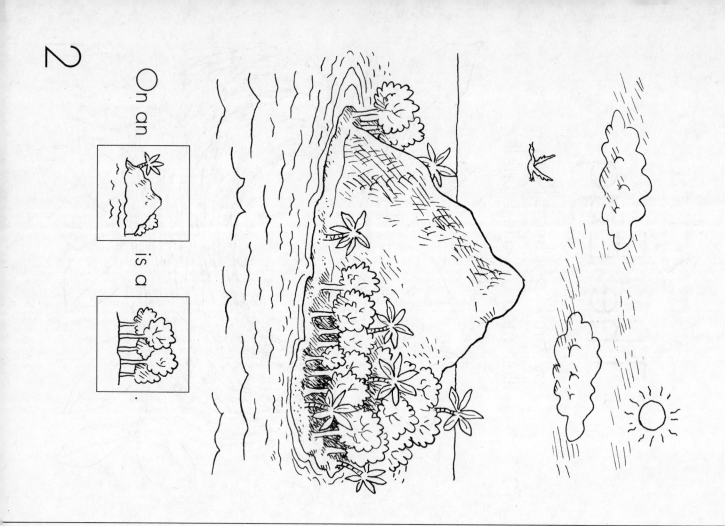 .

In the [ ] is a . . . .

The Egg

by Amy Goldman Koss
illustrated by Julie Durrell

In the ⬭ WAS a 🐦.

8